STANDARDIZED TEST PRACTICE FOR 8TH GRADE

Editor
Lorin Klistoff, M.A.

Editorial Manager
Karen Goldfluss, M.S. Ed.

Editor in Chief
Sharon Coan, M.S. Ed.

Cover Artist
Sue Fullam

Art Coordinator
Denice Adorno

Creative Director
Elayne Roberts

Imaging
James Edward Grace

Product Manager
Phil Garcia

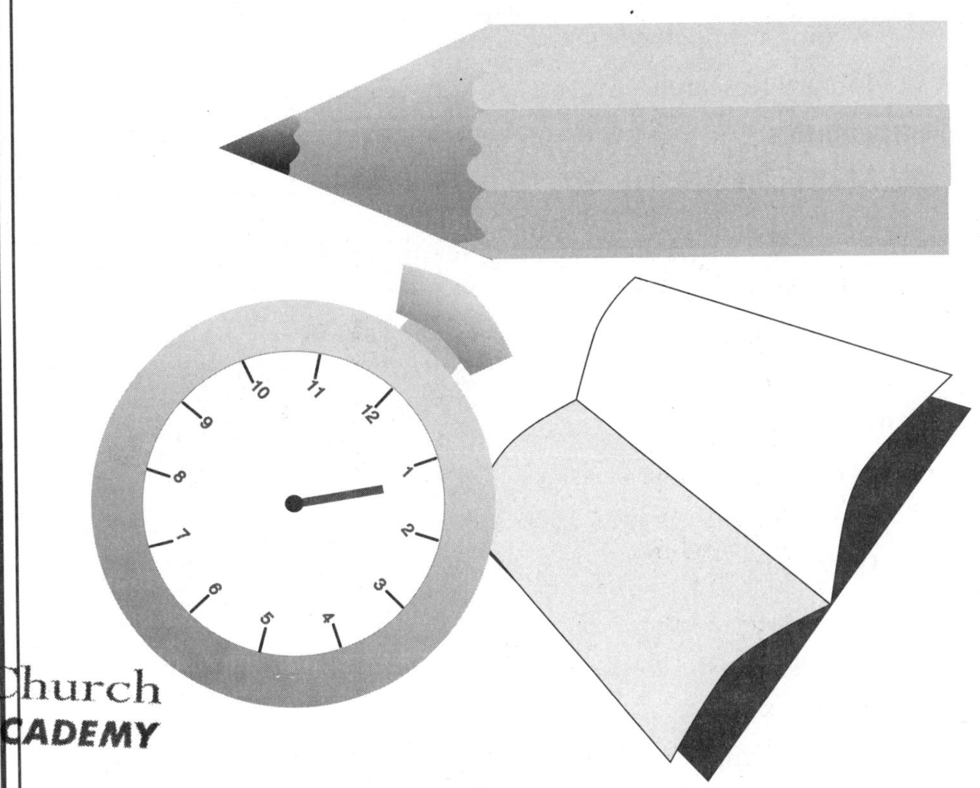

Publishers
Rachelle Cracchiolo, M.S. Ed.
Mary Dupuy Smith, M.S. Ed.

Author

Charles J. Shields

Teacher Created Materials, Inc.
6421 Industry Way
Westminster, CA 92683
www.teachercreated.com

Made in U.S.A.

ISBN-1-57690-683-3

Table of Contents

Introduction

You have undoubtedly given plenty of tests during your years of teaching—unit tests, pop quizzes, final exams, and yes, standardized tests. As a professional educator, you know that standardized tests have taken on an importance greater than any of the others.

No one who understands children and the nature of learning would argue that a standardized test provides a measure of a child's understanding, a teacher's effectiveness, or a school's performance. It is a statistical snapshot of a group of children on a particular day. And there is no "generic child." Take a look at a girl named Joanna, for instance. Reluctant to speak during discussions or participate in group work, she's a whiz at taking tests and scores high on formal tests. However, Dion, in the seat beside her, is creative but impulsive. He dawdles during timed tests and sometimes fills in the wrong answer section. His score? It is no more a true indication of his ability than his doodles of motorcycle-riding monsters in the margins of his papers. You are probably thinking of a Joanna or a Dion in your class right now.

However, schools must be accountable to their communities. Moreover, issues of equity and opportunity for children require that some method of checking all students' progress, as objectively as possible, be administered annually or even semi-annually. As a result, at the insistence of parents, school boards, state legislatures, and national commissions, standardized tests and their results are receiving more attention now than at any other time during the last 35 years.

The purpose of this book is to help you and your students get better results on standardized tests. The exercises are grade-specific and based on the most recent versions of these testing instruments:

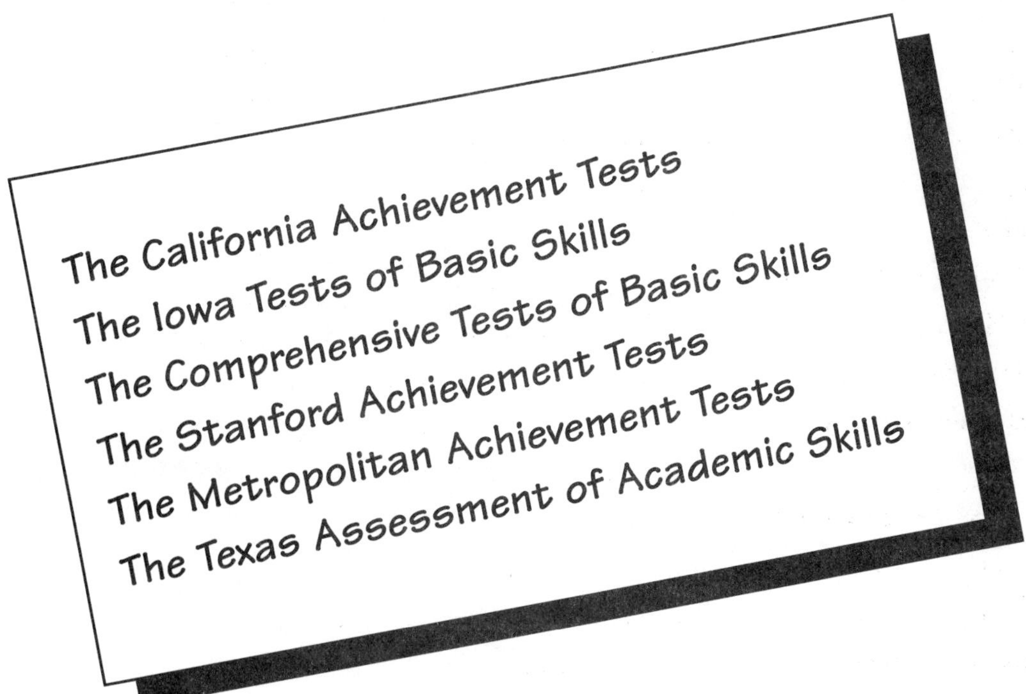

Exercise materials designed for this book reflect skills from curricula, grade-level tests, and test taking from the California Academic Standards Commission, the New York State Testing Program for Elementary and Intermediate Grades, the Texas Essential Knowledge and Skills program, and the Board of Education for the Commonwealth of Virginia. Your students can expect to meet again, on widely used standardized tests, most of the content in this book and the style in which questions are posed.

About the Practice Tests

You will notice several things right away about the exercises.

1. The tests are arranged by curricular topics: grammar, reading comprehension, or geometry, for example.
2. The exercises are short enough that you can integrate them into your teaching day. If you spend 20 minutes daily on test taking over several weeks as you approach a test date, your students will build confidence and increase their knowledge base in preparation for the actual test. Becoming familiar with testing formats and practicing on sample questions is one of the most effective ways to improve scores.

Each section of the book—Language Arts, Mathematics, Science, Social Studies, Fine Arts, Computers and Technology—begins with a short lesson for students about answering the questions in that section and includes a list of test-taking tips. It would be a good idea to have your students take turns reading portions of the lesson aloud so you can emphasize key suggestions.

Ways to Increase Students' Confidence

- Downplay the importance of how many right answers versus how many wrong answers your students give. These exercises generally have the same purpose as drills in sports—to improve players' ability through regular practice. Fill the role of coach as students learn to hit the long ball.
- Give credit for reasonable answers. Encourage students to explain why they answered as they did. Praise thoughtfulness and good guesses. Surprise them by giving partial credit because their logic is persuasive. On some state-designed tests, credit is given for "almost right" answers.
- Promote in your classroom a positive, relaxed feeling about test taking. It might be wise, for example, to put off administering a planned practice from this booklet if your students are anxious or feeling overwhelmed about something. Use a little psychology in strengthening the association in their minds between test taking and opportunities to feel pleased about themselves.

Skills Index

The following pages provide a list of the basic skills embedded in the tests in this book.

Language Arts

Reading

Uses knowledge of word formation, sentence structure, or other context clues.

Supports argument or opinion by reference to evidence presented in sources.

Uses print and electronic catalogs and indices to locate materials.

Constructs meaning from literary, informational, and practical texts.

Reads informational and practical material with complex vocabulary, concepts, and formats independently.

Recognizes the characteristics of persuasive text.

Recognizes coherence, logic, and organization in persuasive text.

Recognizes relatedness and sufficiency of details in persuasive text.

Extracts ideas embedded in complex passages of text.

Recognizes the author's bias.

Writing

Understands and uses stages in the writing process independently.

Uses literary devices and design elements as appropriate to describe, support an opinion, or persuade an audience.

Edits work for errors in sentence formation, usage, mechanics, and spelling.

Mathematics

Rational and Irrational Numbers

Compares and orders rational numbers in meaningful contexts.

Expresses whole numbers in scientific notation; converts scientific notation to standard form.

Uses exponential notation to express prime factorization of numbers less than 100.

Uses estimation techniques with rational numbers.

Real Numbers

Estimates and solves problems using ratios, proportions, and percent.

Applies concepts of ratio, proportion, and percent to real life situations, such as consumer applications, science, and social studies.

Uses real-world examples or models to represent multiplication and division of integers; records and explains procedures used.

Geometry

Uses geometric models to develop the meaning of the square and the positive square root of a number.

Relates concepts of ratio, proportion, and percent in meaningful context.

Demonstrates an understanding and uses properties and relationships of geometry.

Uses the properties and relationships of geometry to solve problems.

Identifies applications of geometry in the environment.

Graphs shapes and congruent figures on a coordinate plane.

Mathematics *(cont.)*

Pre-Algebra

Demonstrates an understanding of patterns and pre-algebra.
Describes, extends, analyzes, and creates a wide variety of patterns to investigate relationships and solve problems.
Uses the concept of operations with variables.
Solves simple linear equations.
Investigates and evaluates algebraic expressions using mental calculations, pencil, paper, and calculators where appropriate.

Science

Biology

Understands the structure and reproduction of invertebrates.
Understands various types of seeds and how they function.
Identifies how genetics is the cell transmission of traits.
Recognizes traits of the human nervous system.

Chemistry

Defines matter as a part of nature.
Identifies changes in matter.
Understands the arrangement of elements on the periodic table.

Physics

Describes motion.
Explains the characteristics of light and heat.
Explains the characteristics of electricity and magnetism.
Identifies sources of different kinds of energy.

Geology

Identifies the earth's structure.
Understands the nature of forces that change the external features of the earth.
Identifies characteristics of the atmosphere and weather.

Social Studies

World History

Prehistory
Fertile Crescent
Middle Ages
Ancient Asia and Africa
Ancient Greece
Ancient Rome
Ancient Egypt

World Geography

United States History

Fine Arts

Music

Identifies simple musical forms.

Compares in two or more arts how the characteristic materials of each art can be used to transform similar events, scenes, emotions, or ideas into works of art.

Classifies by genre and style a variety of musical works.

Dance

Understands the concept of improvisation.

Understands the concept of composition.

Understands the role of dance in various cultures.

Makes connections between dance and healthful living.

Theater

Recognizes what drama is and how it happens.

Recognizes unique characteristics of the dramatic script.

Understands the difference between actor and character.

Understands and analyzes dramatic elements found in theater, film, television, and electronic media presentations.

Computers and Technology

Demonstrates an understanding of copyright by citing sources of copyrighted materials in papers, projects, and multimedia presentations.

Demonstrates knowledge and skills in the use of computer and other technologies.

Searches and sorts information using more than one criterion and explains the strategies used to find information.

Chooses charts, tables, or graphs to best represent data and states the reason.

Evaluates the information from electronic sources as to validity, appropriateness, content, and usefulness.

Lesson 1: Minding the Minutes

The purpose of this lesson is to help you learn how to answer the most questions you can on a standardized test.

A standardized test is timed. It is another way of trying to make the test fair. It would not be fair to allow some students to spend an hour solving a dozen one-step math problems—which is much longer than necessary—and a second group of students to spend only 15 minutes. Would it be clear who understood the problems better? No, it would not be a fair or an accurate measure of the students' abilities.

Keep in mind that you get credit for the number of questions you answer correctly. The more questions you answer correctly, the higher your score. Keeping this in mind, what do you think you should do when you have a limited amount of time to answer a lot of questions?

To answer this question, imagine what you would do in another situation. You are about to play a game outside. In this game, you have 10 minutes to gather all the pieces of candy you can. The pieces have been hidden in the grass, in the bushes, and next to stones. Some of them are easy to see; some are well-hidden. Now, what would you do?

You would probably run around and pick up all the pieces you could see right away. If you still had time, you could go back and search for the pieces that are well-hidden. But remember—the idea is to get as many pieces of candy as you can. So go for the easy ones first!

Believe it or not, the same strategy works on a standardized test. See for yourself. Here are three math questions that you must finish with only half of a minute left on the test.

---

1. $\frac{2}{6} + \frac{1}{6}$

(A) $^1/_6$
(B) $^3/_{12}$
(C) $^3/_6$
(D) 3
(E) none of these

Fill in the correct circle.

Ⓐ Ⓑ Ⓒ Ⓓ Ⓔ

---

2. $\frac{2}{7} = \frac{?}{35}$

(F) 7
(G) 5
(H) 10
(J) 11
(K) none of these

Fill in the correct circle.

Ⓕ Ⓖ Ⓗ Ⓙ Ⓚ

---

3. $\frac{3}{8} + \frac{1}{4} =$

(A) $^2/_4$
(B) $^2/_8$
(C) $^4/_{12}$
(D) $^4/_8$
(E) none of these

Fill in the correct circle.

Ⓐ Ⓑ Ⓒ Ⓓ Ⓔ

Lesson 1: Minding the Minutes *(cont.)*

You might be able to answer all three problems on the previous page, but if you had to choose, which would you skip? You would probably not try problem 2 since it looks like it would take the longest amount of time to solve.

What if there are 25 math problems on one part of a test and you skipped six of them because they looked like they would take longer to solve? How do you remind yourself to go back? *Put a little check mark on your answer sheet next to each problem you skipped.* If there is time, you can go back and work on the harder problems.

Here is one more example in which you might have to skip questions on a test, but the choice is a little different. What if there are two reading passages on a test—one has four questions after it, and the other one has eight? You think you only have time to read one of the passages. Which one should you choose?

Choose the one with eight questions after it. Maybe you will only have time to answer six of the eight questions, but you will probably get more of them right than if you read the other passage, answered the four questions, and then were reading the second passage when you ran out of time.

Whenever you can, answer correctly as many questions as you can on a standardized test. That's the smart way to mind the minutes.

Lesson 2: Guessing Correctly

This lesson will explain to you that it is possible to answer a question correctly, even if you're just guessing. The secret is narrowing your choices.

Sometimes you will be faced with a really difficult multiple-choice question. It might be that

- you do not understand the question very well.
- you do not understand the answer choices.
- you simply do not know the answer at all.

What should you do? Guess? Yes, you should guess. But you can increase the chance of choosing the correct answer by using a few strategies.

"Best-Guess" Strategies

1. Always make sure to read all the choices.

Do not jump at the first one that looks like it might be right. Here is an example:

Which is the largest city?

(A) Los Angeles
(B) Detroit
(C) Atlanta
(D) New York

Fill in the correct circle.

Ⓐ Ⓑ Ⓒ Ⓓ

Lesson 2: Guessing Correctly *(cont.)*

"Best-Guess" Strategies *(cont.)*

Maybe you do not know which is the largest city, but you do know that (A) "Los Angeles" is bigger than (B) "Detroit," so you choose (A) "Los Angeles" and go on to the next question. But wait! It is important to read all the choices. In fact, (D) "New York" is the largest city. You might have guessed between (A) "Los Angeles" or (D) "New York" if you had read all the possible answers. To be a good guesser, you must read every choice and think about each of them, one at a time. If you are the kind of tester who always reads all the choices before choosing one, then you are doing the right thing.

2. Eliminate the answer choices that are plainly wrong.

Here is an example of a social studies question you might find on a test. Choose the correct term.

How can the president stop a law that has been passed by Congress?

(A) politics
(B) capital
(C) veto
(D) arrest

Fill in the correct circle.

(A) (B) (C) (D)

Think carefully about this situation. Choice (A) "politics" is something like "business" or "teaching"—it is a profession. How could it be used to stop anything? Next, (B) "capital" is usually a place, like a state capital. It could not be used to stop a process like passing a law. What about (D) "arrest"? People do get stopped when they are put "under arrest," but this is a law being talked about, not people, so (D) "arrest" is probably not the correct answer. That leaves (C) "veto" as the most likely choice, because each of the other choices does not quite fit for some reason. If you chose (C) "veto," you would be right.

3. Look carefully for clues about how the word is used.

On some tests, you might run across a reading passage that has vocabulary words that you do not know. Here is an example of such a reading passage.

> In *The Goats* (1987), Brock Cole's first novel, Howie Mitchell and Laura Golden meet at Tall Pine, a summer camp. They recognize each other as outcasts. "I'm socially retarded for my age," Laura tells Howie. "Yeah. Me too," Howie replies. But deep down, neither of them believes those statements. When a cruel practical joke leaves them abandoned on an island, they seize the opportunity to test their self-reliance and independence. They escape from the island, steer clear of their camp, and make do for themselves. They remain on the run until they are confident they have new identities of which they can be proud.

Based on the passage you read, what is the meaning of the word *self-reliance* in this passage?

(A) personal courage
(B) tools
(C) meanness
(D) depending on oneself

Fill in the correct circle.

Lesson 2: Guessing Correctly *(cont.)*

"Best-Guess" Strategies *(cont.)*

In this case, if you do not know the meaning of the word *self-reliance*, you need to look carefully for clues about how the word is used. The passage says Howie and Laura were abandoned on an island and used the "opportunity to test their self-reliance and independence." Why would they test their (C) "meanness" in such a situation? That does not make much sense. And nothing is said about them having (B) "tools." If they had tools, it would not have been a "cruel practical joke" to leave them abandoned on an island. "Tools" is not a good choice. They might have tested their (A) "personal courage," but the passage also said they "make do for themselves" which suggests (D) "depending on oneself." So both (A) and (D) are likely choices, but at least you have eliminated two of the four choices. Now you have a fifty-fifty chance of getting the answer correct. Which do you choose, (A) or (D)? The answer is (D) "depending on oneself."

4. **For a math problem, you can use estimating to help you when you are not sure of the answer.**

Now try this problem.

The choir practiced for 2 $^{3}/_{4}$ hours on Saturday and 3 $^{2}/_{3}$ hours on Sunday. How much was the total time?

(A) 4 $^{3}/_{4}$ hours
(B) 5 $^{17}/_{12}$ hours
(C) 5 $^{7}/_{8}$ hours
(D) 6 $^{5}/_{12}$ hours

Fill in the correct circle.

Ⓐ Ⓑ Ⓒ Ⓓ

Maybe this problem gives you trouble because you have difficulty with fractions. Use estimation to help you make your best guess.

Looking at the whole numbers in the problem, the choir practiced 2 hours + 3 hours which totals 5 hours. Five is more than (A) 4 $^{3}/_{4}$ hours. You know that is true even without adding the fractions. (A) cannot be correct. Next, the mixed number (B) 5 $^{17}/_{12}$ is strange. Have you ever seen a mixed number in which the numerator of the fraction is larger than the denominator? (B) is probably not correct either. (C) 5 $^{7}/_{8}$ is a possibility, but look closely; 8 is not a common denominator of $^{3}/_{4}$ and $^{2}/_{3}$. How could you get an answer like (C) 5 $^{7}/_{8}$? That leaves (D) 6 $^{5}/_{12}$.

If you guessed (D) even without doing the problem, you would be right. You did some quick estimating to solve the problem.

Remember to use these four strategies:

- Make sure to read all the answer choices.
- Eliminate choices that are plainly wrong.
- Look for clues about how a word is used.
- Estimate the answer.

You are sure to raise your test scores if you practice guessing correctly.

Introduction

The language arts section of standardized tests always involves a lot of reading. There are short questions, too, of course, but quite often you must read a paragraph or a long passage to answer the questions.

Here's the Idea

To answer your best on the language arts sections, you must be able to do the following:

1. Identify main ideas.
2. Recognize important details or clues.
3. Draw conclusions on your own.

Before we look at each of the three skills, read the following tips that apply to taking any test, whether it is in language arts, mathematics, science, social studies, fine arts, or computers and technology. These tips will be repeated because they are important!

Test-Taking Tips

- **Read directions carefully before marking any test questions**, even though you have done that kind of test before. You may think you already know what the directions say, but don't ignore them—read them over. If you do not understand the directions, raise your hand and ask for help. Although your teacher must read the directions exactly as they are written, the teacher can make sure you understand what the directions mean.
- **Follow instructions.** Pay close attention to the sample exercises. They will help you understand what the items on the test will be like and how to mark your answer sheet properly.
- **Read the entire question and all the answer choices.** Do not stop reading when you have found a correct answer. Choices D or E may read "B and D" or "all of the above." On some tests, two answers are both correct or possibly none of the answers is correct. You need to read all the answer choices before marking your answer.
- **For long reading passages, read the questions first so you know what to look for.** If you read the questions first, you will find information in the passage that answers questions.
- **Remember that taking a test is not a race!** There are no prizes for finishing first. Use all of the time provided for the test. If you have time left over, check your answers.

Try and Discuss

Now let's discuss the same three skills (*identifying main ideas, recognizing important details or clues,* and *drawing conclusions on your own*) for language arts tests.

Take a look at the question below.

Which one names the whole group?

(A) Earth
(B) Mercury
(C) Pluto
(D) solar system
(E) orbits

Fill in the correct circle.

Ⓐ Ⓑ Ⓒ Ⓓ Ⓔ

One of these words includes all of the others. It is (D) "solar system." The planets—Earth, Mercury, and Pluto—are all part of the solar system, and all the planets travel in an orbit in the solar system.

The main idea of a paragraph is just like that—it is an idea that names all of the other ideas in the paragraph by making them one group. You will be asked to identify main ideas on language arts tests. You also may be asked, "What would be a good title for this?" which is another way of asking, "What is the main idea?"

This time, look at the list of words below and decide what is the main idea of this group. (**Hint: The main idea is not mentioned!**)

What is the main idea that connects these things?

(A) candles
(B) games
(C) ice cream
(D) cake
(E) gifts
(F) guests

What do you think? ______________________________

Think of a main idea that would include all of these things. You might come to the conclusion that the answer is a *birthday party*. In this case, you have to draw your own conclusion. In other words, you have to make a good guess at what the main idea is, even though it does not appear in words.

Sometimes the main idea of a paragraph is given in words directly—as in the solar system example above—but sometimes the main idea is only suggested, as in the birthday party example.

Try and Discuss *(cont.)*

Now take a look at an actual paragraph. You decide what the main idea is.

Welcome Pool Members!

Welcome to the Millertown pool, created by the parks and recreation department for all residents of Millertown. Please keep in mind that many people use the pool in the summer and that rules must be followed. First, running, pushing, or shoving is never allowed. Walk slowly. Second, do not jump from the side of the pool. You might land on someone and hurt the person. Use the diving board for jumping instead. Third, it is good to have fun in the pool, but no rough play is permitted. If the lifeguard sees dangerous behavior, the swimmers will be told to stop immediately. Enjoy yourself while you're here—Millertown pool is for everyone!

The main idea of this paragraph is

(A) summer.
(B) swimming.
(C) pool safety.
(D) having fun.

Fill in the correct circle.

Ⓐ Ⓑ Ⓒ Ⓓ

This paragraph is an example of one of those times when you must both recognize important details or clues and draw conclusions on your own.

Eliminate choices by looking for details. For example, you might think that (A) "summer" is correct because, after all, people go to a pool in the summer. But look closely. How many details are about summer in the paragraph? The summer months are not mentioned; the temperature in the summertime is not mentioned. There are no details about summer.

How about choice (B) "swimming"? The paragraph is all about swimming or, at least, using the pool. But in fact, there are no details about how to swim or when to swim. Most of the details—"walk slowly" and "no rough play"—are about safety at the pool. So (C) "pool safety" is the correct answer. What about (D) "having fun"? Draw your own conclusion; see how many details about having fun you can find in the paragraph.

Tips That Help

Remember the following tips:

- The main idea in a paragraph covers all the other ideas in the paragraph or passage.
- Sometimes you must draw your own conclusion. Look for details that support your good guess about what the main idea is.

Now try the practice tests. Follow the test directions and solve the sample problems to be sure you understand what to do on each test.

Directions: Read the verse below, and fill in the circle of the correct response for each question.

You Mustn't Quit

When things go wrong, as they sometimes will,
When the road you're trudging seems all uphill,
When the funds are low and the debts are high
And you want to smile, but you have to sigh,
When care is pressing you down a bit,
Rest! if you must—but never quit.
Life is queer, with its twists and turns,
As every one of us sometimes learns,
And many a failure turns about
When he might have won if he'd stuck it out;
Stick to your task, though the pace seems slow—
You may succeed with one more blow.
Success is failure turned inside out—
The silver tint of the clouds of doubt—
And you never can tell how close you are,
It may be near when it seems afar;
So stick to the fight when you're hardest hit—
It's when things seem worst that YOU MUSTN'T QUIT.

—Author Unknown

1. Each set of six lines is called a
   - (A) chorus.
   - (B) stanza.
   - (C) verse.
   - (D) paragraph.

2. The accented and unaccented syllables in each line is called
   - (F) rhythm.
   - (G) beats.
   - (H) meter.
   - (J) stress.

3. The rhyme scheme of "You Mustn't Quit" is
   - (A) abcdef.
   - (B) ababcc.
   - (C) abacdd.
   - (D) aabbcc.

4. The "clouds of doubt" is a figure of speech called a
   - (F) simile.
   - (G) ideal.
   - (H) metaphor.
   - (J) rondo.

5. The writing device used in phrases such as "the funds are low and the debts are high" and "It may be near when it seems afar" is called
   - (A) singsong.
   - (B) contrast.
   - (C) sameness.
   - (D) surprise.

6. This piece of verse is about
   - (F) using your money wisely.
   - (G) getting somewhere fast.
   - (H) learning how to do things right.
   - (J) having a winning attitude.

➢ **STOP** ➣

Directions: Read each of the following passages. Choose a title that best summarizes the main idea of the passage.

It's noon on Easter Monday in Dublin, Ireland, 1916. The pedestrians on Sackville Street, the city's main thoroughfare, hardly glance up from their window—shopping as a troop of a few dozen men, wearing both civilian and military dress, march to a halt in front of the General Post Office—the GPO, as Dubliners call it.

Most bystanders, including several policemen and British officers, think it's some kind of parade forming. Many of the men in the column have rifles; others have tools: ropes, hammers, picks—a few even carry pikes, an ancient battle-weapon. Accompanying them are three or four vehicles, including an ordinary Ford touring car.

Then a burly man at front of the marchers, shouts, "Left turn! GPO, charge!"

The men break ranks and run through the post office doorway, ordering startled customers to get out of the way. The crack of gunfire sends clerks leaping over their counters. People inside make a rush for the street. Rapidly, the invaders erect barricades and prepare the attack they know is coming.

The "Easter Rising," as it will come to be called in Irish history, has begun. The fight will pit approximately 1,600 Irish citizen-soldiers against the might of the British Empire. The prize—depending on which side you're on—is either Irish independence, or the arrest and punishing of a rag-tag band of traitors.

1. (A) What Happened One Day Long Ago
   (B) The First Shots in the Fight for Irish Independence
   (C) An Attack on a Post Office
   (D) How the British Stopped the "Easter Rising"

Someone is dying.

He sits propped up in bed, struggling to make desperate changes to his final will. His stubborn, uneducated daughter has secretly married a man—a drunk and a cheat—whom he despises. Now he must box them in with words, hastily adding a paragraph even as death approaches. His attorney, family members, and friends watch him cross out names, add phrases, smudging the ink with a puffy hand that is growing uncontrollably weak.

But he's determined to have his way—they won't get their paws on his silver plate, his furniture, or his property! He groans as he writes, trying to make the slithery words legible.

Beside the bed, his wife and daughter begin a hissing, angry quarrel about who should get what.

For the sake of peace, the dying man turns to the last page of his will and squeezes in a final, smeary line: "Itm I gyve unto my wief my second best bed wth the furniture." [Item: I give to my wife my second best bed with the furniture.]

He signs, "By me William Shakespeare." Six witnesses scribble their names at the bottom of the page. Minutes later, the Western world's greatest playwright dies.

2. (F) How One Man Settled a Quarrel
   (G) Picture of a Dying Man
   (H) Why do People Make Out Their Wills?
   (J) The Surprising Final Moments of William Shakespeare

GO →

Mental illness was once called "madness" or "insanity," terms that are no longer regarded as scientific because they are too general. In addition, what seems "mad" to one society may not seem so to another. The Greek historian Herodotus, writing in the mid-5th century B.C., argued that King Cambyses of Persia was mad. Why? Because Cambyses ridiculed holy services honoring the gods and made fun of tradition. In today's societies, especially democratic ones, such behavior might draw criticism, but it would probably not be equated with mental illness. In Herodotus's opinion, however, Cambyses's behavior could only come from a mind "gone mad."

3. (A) Ridiculing the Gods: the First Sign of Insanity
   (B) What People Once Meant by "Madness"
   (C) Foolish Mistakes About Strange Behavior
   (D) Mental Illness

One day, a long time ago, when it was hot—when the radio said that maybe a hurricane from the Gulf of Mexico was coming our way—I saw a man standing at our mailbox by the edge of the road. You could tell he worked in the fields. He looked sort of beat down, but strong. There were dark stains of sweat on his blue shirt. He rested one hand on the mailbox and stood there studying our name, Ochoa, painted in red. From his pocket, he pulled out a handkerchief and rubbed his neck all around.

"Who's that?" asked my little brother Nando. We were in the yard feeding chickens.

The man looked up at us, squinted, and tipped his hat. "Is your father at home?" he called. "Someone I may speak to?"

"My father, yes," I said.

"Good, OK." He smiled and pushed his hat back on.

"He's coming," I said. "Quick, get Daddy."

Nando twisted his toe in the dirt. "Naw, I want to stay."

"Do as I say or I'll pull your hair—get going!"

Nando trotted off in the direction of the porch, looking back over his shoulder.

As the man walked up the drive, he passed our pickup truck, freshly washed. He paused and looked at it admiringly as if it belonged to him.

"Can I help you?" I said, crossing my arms.

The stranger came close. His perspiring brown face broke into a grin.

"Perhaps, senorita." Several of his teeth were gold.

4. (F) The Hurricane
   (G) Little Brothers are That Way
   (H) The Stranger
   (J) Our Farm by the Road

Directions: An *inference* is a conclusion you draw on your own. For example, if you tried to turn on a TV and nothing happened, you would make the inference that the TV isn't working.

Read the following passages. Choose the statement you think is a correct inference.

I didn't have a very interesting life—or even a very interesting job, for that matter. If I had, it might have been some comfort in coping with my loneliness.

I worked for a large advertising firm in Chicago, right on the Magnificent Mile overlooking the river. When I would tell people that, they'd say, "What a wonderful job for a young woman, how exciting!" But the truth is, the key to advertising is making people think they want something—making them believe they have to have it to be happy. And as the years passed, I began to realize the irony of selling dreams when my own dreams had gone unfilled.

1. (A) The speaker is very proud of her job.
   (B) The speaker is upset that the company she works for doesn't know about her dreams.
   (C) The speaker's job is to sell her dreams to others.
   (D) The speaker feels her life isn't working out.

Bing!

"Val, order up!"

Inside Kilroy's breakfast shop, standing at a table near the jukebox is Valerie Kilroy, slightly harassed owner/waitress of a failing business left to her by her granddad Willard Kilroy. At the table she's waiting on, two elderly ladies are trying make up their minds how they want their eggs.

"Let's see now, let's see now. Scrambled hard? No, I don't like 'em that way. Do you, Effie?" said the one old lady with a brown hat like a crushed flowerpot.

"What?" said the other pleasantly.

"Like 'em scrambled hard?"

"Oh, heavens no! My Bill always used to say—"

"So ladies!" Val interrupted, feeling her patience slipping, "Scrambled easy?"

Both powdery ladies act nervous, as if this were a decision that neither of them would ever dare make on her own.

"Valerie!" *Bing*! *Bing*! "Order—"

"Hold your horses, Jeff!" Val shot him a dirty look over the heads of customers and caught him grinning back there in the kitchen. Tom, the assistant cook, slapped Jeff on the back, as if watching their boss lose her cool was the best time they'd had in a week.

"You'll get yours, numbskulls," she muttered.

"Excuse me, dear?" said in the lady in the flowerpot hat.

2. (F) Two boys are teasing a girl in a cafeteria.
   (G) It's a busy morning a breakfast shop, and the owner is also a waitress.
   (H) Two old ladies are the owners of a breakfast shop.
   (J) A girl's grandfather makes her waitress in a breakfast shop.

GO →

He introduced himself, then rested his chin on his hand and trained his gorgeous cornflower blue eyes on me. "Look, you're going to think I'm crazy," he began, "I mean, you probably don't even know who I am."

"I know who you are." My mouth was dry.

"You do? Hey, all right! Well, homecoming is a couple of weeks away, and I was wondering—has anybody asked you yet?"

I shook my head.

"Would you like to go? With me?"

Before I even realized the word was out of my mouth, I said "Yes."

On the way home on the bus, I blurted out the whole situation to my best friend, Jeanine.

"Your mom has to let you go, that's all there is to it," she said firmly. "Homecoming is next month. You're going to be fifteen in December anyway. What is the difference between fifteen and sixteen?"

"You're right," I agreed. "That's just what I'm going to say. What's the difference between fifteen and sixteen?"

3. (A) The boy who asked the girl to the dance isn't old enough to date.
   (B) The date of the dance is December 15th or 16th.
   (C) The girl was too embarrassed to tell the boy "no."
   (D) The girl is afraid her mother won't let her go because she's too young.

I hug the magazine tightly and look up at the clouds turning orange as the day ends. "Please, God," I whisper. "Let me into this world I want so badly. I'll be content for anything, just so long as I can be in the movies."

"Uh-oh, here she comes, Miss Beverly Hills! More like Miss Beverly Hillbilly, if you ask me." My brother Bob grins at me from the steps of the front porch while scraping mud off his boots with a stick.

"Shut up!" I say, walking toward him menacingly. "Just because you want to spend your life feeding chickens and shoveling out stalls doesn't mean I have to."

"And what's wrong with that kind of life?" says my dad, coming around the side of the house.

I feel bad—I blurted out something that might have hurt him. But I can't bear to think that I'm never going to have my dreams.

"Let me see that," he says, holding out one big hand, rough and dirty from working in the field all day.

"It's nothing, it's just one of my movie magazines." But he continues to hold out his hand stiffly until I give him the magazine from behind my back.

"Jessica Anne, this is just a lot of nonsense," he says flipping through the pages. "You'd be better off reading that church magazine your mother got you a subscription to. It'll help you more than this muck."

"It's not muck! It's joy and happiness and—*and the world*! A much bigger world than the one we got around here! I'll just die if I can't be a part of it."

My dad stands with his thumbs hooked in the braces of his overalls, looking down at me. He rubs his sunburned, whiskered face thoughtfully. "You go in and help your mother set the table," is all he says, as if something has just occurred to him.

"Yes, sir." I stomp miserably up the porch steps.

4. (F) The girl used to be in movies and now she's not.
   (G) The girl lives on a farm and wants to go to Hollywood.
   (H) The girl doesn't know what she wants and her dad is angry.
   (J) The girl hasn't been going to church and her father is going to punish her.

Directions: Read the passage below, and answer the questions.

Book Review

(*Party Girl* by Lynne Ewing. Knopf, New York. 110 pages.)

Party Girl is the story of Kata, a Hispanic gangbanger in East Los Angeles, whose best friend Ana is killed in a drive-by shooting. Kata is living "the life" as her "compadres" call it, although she realizes it isn't much of one. Ana was Kata's emotional anchor. But with her gone, Kata is getting increasingly tired of the tough guy posing, the boozing, the terror of death, and the loneliness that assaults her. She tries to connect with someone who can lift her above this landscape of despair, but no one really can. Finally, her own spirituality demands that she take herself out of "the life" by choice, a thoughtful solution for which author Ewing deserves praise. It's not because Kata changes schools, or gets a job, or benefits from a social service program that she changes her life. Ewing seems to be saying that young people are naturally good, and the souls of human beings, especially children, are not suited for dealing with relentless cruelty.

Ewing, a former social worker before turning to writing, expertly describes the culture of Hispanic gangs. Layers of Mexican and South American myth, Catholicism, and African/Jamaican rituals create a kind of romantic hopelessness. Kids attend traditional funerals for their murdered friends, pose by the coffins throwing up gang signs, and later tattoo a teardrop under one eye. The suggestion is that the call to join a gang comes at a time in a young person's life when he or she wants to belong to something bigger, more important. Kata is almost, but not quite, taken in by the false promise offered by gangs in this excellent book.

1. The setting of this book is
   (A) New York.
   (B) a Catholic Church.
   (C) the city streets.
   (D) East Los Angeles.

2. The conflict in this book is
   (F) most people don't like gangbangers.
   (G) Kata's friend is murdered.
   (H) too many different people live near each other.
   (J) Kata wants to leave the gang life.

3. The type of conflict in this book is
   (A) man versus nature.
   (B) man versus himself.
   (C) man versus technology.
   (D) man versus the supernatural.

4. In *Party Girl,* the author seems to say that
   (F) more money is needed to put an end to gangs.
   (G) young people are naturally good but sometimes need gangs.
   (H) violence makes young people grow up.
   (J) gangs get mixed up with religion.

5. The writer of this book review thinks the author of *Party Girl*
   (A) gives too much information about gangs.
   (B) doesn't need to talk about so many different subjects.
   (C) does a good job of explaining how gangs work.
   (D) thinks this book will encourage young people to join gangs.

➢ **STOP** ➣

Directions: Read each passage, and answer the questions that follow.

He never learned to drive a car, wrote all his works on a typewriter, and disliked the Internet, but author Ray Bradbury captured the dizzying effects of change better than any other popular American writer of the 20th century. Author of more than 500 published works which included short stories, novels, plays, screenplays, television scripts, and verse, Bradbury's fiction explored the possibilities, joys, and terrors of abandoning the comfortable past and experimenting with the future.

Bradbury was born in his grandparents' house, August 22, 1920, in Waukegan, Illinois, the third son of an electrical lineman and a homemaker. As a boy, his imagination thrilled to horror films, comic strips, circuses and carnivals, and magic acts. At the local library, he found more of what he was seeking in books by writers such as Edgar Allen Poe, Jules Verne (*20,000 Leagues Under the Sea*), H. G. Wells (*The Time Machine*) and Edgar Rice Burroughs ("Tarzan" and "Martian" novels). Classmates teased him so much about his devotion to futuristic fantasies that one day in the fifth-grade, he came home and tore up his comic book collection of *Buck Rogers in the 25th Century*. But much later, as a successful writer, he commented that he enjoyed rereading those kinds of comic strips as much as he enjoyed the works of great writers. The important thing, he said, was to read.

Which of the following statements is NOT true?

1. (A) Ray Bradbury is old-fashioned in his personal life.
   (B) Because Bradbury's classmates teased him, he decided to give up thinking about the future.
   (C) Bradbury's interest in the future goes back to when he was a boy.
   (D) Bradbury enjoys comic strips as much a the works of great writers.

According to the Center for Mental Health, "the number of families who are affected by mental, emotional, and behavioral disorders in young people is staggering. It is estimated that as many as one in five children or adolescents may have a mental health problem that can be identified and treated." (Abrahamson, 254) In addition, figures provided to the center by the National Institute for Mental Health indicate that at least one in 10—or as many as six million young people—may have a "serious emotional disturbance." (Fitch, 113) This term refers to a mental health problem that severely disrupts a person's ability to function socially, academically, and emotionally. You'd expect that more children would be identified by schools as needing help, given this kind of data, but many children are not getting the treatment they need. Schools need more funding and better resources to identify students' mental health problems.

Which of the following statements is NOT true?

2. (F) Children are getting mental health problems because of school.
   (G) Mental health problems can be identified and treated.
   (H) Schools could do a better job of identifying children who need help.
   (J) One in five children may have a mental health problem.

GO →

Directions: Read each passage, and answer the questions that follow.

Obesity is a number one health problem in the United States. One out of every two Americans is overweight. Those who are obese are getting fatter each year, and the number of fat people is increasing each year. In fact, some authorities describe obesity as the United States' special form of malnutrition. The number of obese Americans ranks in the millions. Although many people go on diets each month, few are successful in permanently shedding their extra pounds. Obesity plagues teenagers as well as adults. According to Mrs. Mary Shea, the school nurse at Nickels High School, for example, fifty percent of the students are overweight while twenty percent of those are actually obese.

Which of the following statements is NOT true?

3. (A) More people are getting fatter every year.
   (B) Few people succeed at dieting.
   (C) Half of Americans are overweight.
   (D) Twenty percent of students at Nickels High School are overweight.

Women's legal rights in Ancient Egypt were respected, as shown by marriage contracts from the era of the New Kingdom (1550 B.C.–1070 B.C.) and later. In a contract dating from around 580 B.C., a man about to be married takes an oath that if he leaves his wife, he will return the dowry and a share of all the property for the children.

A surprising fact explained why women in Ancient Egypt enjoyed a great deal of legal power. The reason women had substantial rights was due partly to the fact that inheritance was through the female line. When a man married an heiress, he enjoyed her property only so long as she lived. On her death it passed to her daughter and her daughter's husband. Historically, the wife of the king was an heiress. The king came to the throne by right of the marriage with her, not by his birth. He could be of any rank. He at once became king when he married the queen.

One way to think of women's status in Ancient Egypt is to imagine married men today hyphenating their last names to show equality with their wives.

Which of the following statements is NOT true?

4. (F) Any man could become king in Ancient Egypt.
   (G) A woman's property was her own in Ancient Egypt.
   (H) Men in Ancient Egypt had to take an oath swearing they would not leave their wives.
   (J) Legally, husbands could use their wife's property only so long as she lived.

Directions: Identify the part of speech for each underlined word or words. In some cases, you will be asked to identify the type of sentence: declarative, interrogative, exclamatory, or imperative; simple, compound, or complex.

How to Go Up a Grade in Every Class

It's the start of a new year, and no matter whether you've received poor grades in a
1 2
subject—or several subjects before—you can get better grades starting immediately. In fact, if
3
you follow just some of the advice below, it's almost a sure bet you'll go up at least one grade
in those same subjects with which you used to have such trouble.
4

Here's what to do: First, make a folder for each class. If you've been cramming all your
handouts, maps, homework, and graded tests into one notebook, stop! You're making it hard on
5 6
yourself for the following reasons: (A) It's not easy to get a sense of what's been covered in one
class when papers from all your classes are shuffled like a deck of cards. Assign one folder for
7
each, and put the papers in order by units or chronologically. And *viola*! Now you can see step-
7 8
by-step what you're doing in each class. In addition, if your work is out of order, it's tough to
8
study for a test. Many times, you'll be asked on a test to explain a process or a historical
development. If your papers are mixed up, odds are you will be, too. (B) Finally, with everything
9
stuffed into one notebook, you're taking a big chance. Lose that notebook, and you'll be in
10
trouble. Just imagine, you'll only have class text—nothing else. All the extra information and
10 11
examples your teacher has shared will be gone!
11

GO →

How to Go Up a Grade in Every Class *(cont.)*

Second, save everything. Break the habit of looking at the grade on a test or quiz, then throwing your work away. Those tests, in particular, are your aces in the hole when it comes to getting better grades (12). Here's a secret: teachers don't come up with new questions for major tests. They (13) go back and pull out important ones from earlier tests and quizzes. That (14) way, they know whether you're really learning the material. And to be honest, any teacher will tell (15) you that new questions—worthwhile ones—are hard to create. So they pull out those old show-stoppers (16) one more time—be ready!

Third, get an assignment notebook. Here's the kind of situation you don't want to be in: you're at your locker after school. The bus is leaving (17) in a couple of minutes. You're racing through your mind trying to remember what you have for homework. You think you have all the books you need, and you sprint to the bus (18). Then halfway home—oh, no! You (19) forgot your English book. There's no way you can answer those poetry questions because you don't have the poems (20). A better system is to write down your assignments day-by-day in a little notebook and (21) flip through it as you stand at your locker. You can even plan ahead and erase some of that anxiety that's caused by feeling unsure all the time about what's due.

Fourth, stay a step ahead. Is there some rule that says you're "not allowed" to read the next (22)

GO →

How to Go Up a Grade in Every Class *(cont.)*

chapter before it's covered in class? Think what a genius you'll look like in class when you can
22
ask questions or make comments that indicate you know where the teacher's headed. Hey, you
23
must be psychic! On a practical level, knowing the direction of the class will make the work
23
seem logical—who needs a daily trip into the confusing unknown?
24

Fifth, average your points regularly. Just designate a page in your folder, even the cover, as
25
the place where you list your grades. Assign each one a point value, and find the average. If
26
you're missing a grade or your total isn't working out, ask your teacher for help after class. By
27
monitoring what you're getting, you won't be surprised by a low final grade when it's too late to
28 29
raise it.
29

Sixth, participate in class. It's so easy just to drift along, half-listening to a discussion.
Snap yourself back into focus by thinking of a question or by volunteering your opinion. This
will keep you alert. And there's another benefit, too: the teacher will remember, when it's time
30
for final grades, how you helped out. Everyone in a class learns faster when there's participation.
31

Last, spread out your studying—don't cram. Sure, there are many student "war stories"
32
about staying up until midnight studying and then getting an "A" on the test the next day,
nevertheless. But do you know what? You retain information when you review it over time. This
33 34
means you should study lightly for a test a few days before it; then bear down early in the evening
35

GO →

How to Go Up a Grade in Every Class *(cont.)*

the night before; and finally, get up a half-hour early the day of the test and review for it one more time. You'll be prepared, rested, and confident.

Overall, <u>a big part of getting good grades</u> (36) is just being ready for class; having read the assignments regularly; <u>having participated in class</u> (37); and having studied for tests in an organized way. And, of course, that might seem easier said than done. But is being disorganized and careening toward poor grades year after year worth the stress instead? If that were a test question, you'd know the answer.

1. (A) adjective
   (B) adverb
   (C) noun

2. (F) direct object
   (G) verb
   (H) adverb

3. (A) adverb
   (B) adjective
   (C) verb

4. (F) simple sentence
   (G) verb phrase
   (H) prepositional phrase

5. (A) subjects
   (B) nouns
   (C) prepositions

6. (F) conjunction
   (G) interjection
   (H) noun

7. (A) interrogative sentence
   (B) imperative sentence
   (C) exclamatory sentence

8. (F) simple sentence
   (G) compound sentence
   (H) complex sentence

9. (A) interrogative sentence
   (B) imperative sentence
   (C) declarative sentence

10. (F) simple sentence
    (G) complex sentence
    (H) compound sentence

11. (A) exclamatory sentence
    (B) declarative sentence
    (C) imperative sentence

12. (F) simple sentence
    (G) independent clause
    (H) dependent clause

13. (A) demonstrative pronoun
    (B) indefinite pronoun
    (C) personal pronoun

14. (F) personal pronoun
    (G) demonstrative pronoun
    (H) indefinite pronoun

GO →

15. (A) adverb
    (B) verb
    (C) participle

16. (F) verb
    (G) direct object
    (H) indirect object

17. (A) adverb
    (B) adjective
    (C) simple predicate

18. (F) simple sentence
    (G) complex sentence
    (H) compound sentence

19. (A) noun
    (B) simple subject
    (C) adjective

20. (F) simple sentence
    (G) compound sentence
    (H) complex sentence

21. (A) interjection
    (B) linking verb
    (C) conjunction

22. (F) declarative sentence
    (G) exclamatory sentence
    (H) interrogative sentence

23. (A) simple sentence
    (B) complex sentence
    (C) compound sentence

24. (F) verb
    (G) adverb
    (H) participle

25. (A) imperative sentence
    (B) interrogative sentence
    (C) declarative sentence

26. (F) compound sentence
    (G) complex sentence
    (H) simple sentence

27. (A) verb
    (B) adverb
    (C) conjunction

28. (F) verb
    (G) adjective
    (H) gerund

29. (A) relative clause
    (B) prepositional phrase
    (C) simple sentence

30. (F) verb
    (G) direct object
    (H) complete predicate

31. (A) simple sentence
    (B) compound sentence
    (C) complex sentence

32. (F) gerund
    (G) adjective
    (H) adverb

33. (A) interrogative sentence
    (B) declarative sentence
    (C) exclamatory sentence

34. (F) complete predicate
    (G) simple predicate
    (H) prepositional phrase

35. (A) prepositional phrase
    (B) simple predicate
    (C) simple subject

36. (F) prepositional phrase
    (G) complete subject
    (H) simple predicate

37. (A) verb
    (B) participial phrase
    (C) gerund phrase

What's a gerund? ➤ **STOP** ➤

Directions: Read the newspaper editorial below. Then write a letter to the editor either agreeing or disagreeing with the writer's opinion. Your letter should be persuasive and include the following:

- introduction
- 3–5 paragraphs of 4–6 sentences each
- 2–3 reasons for agreeing or disagreeing with the editorial
- conclusion

Compulsory Attendance Laws—Get Rid of 'Em

Several times a year, the administrators at schools meet to discuss the topic "Let's Raise Test Scores." After a few remarks from the principal about the importance of raising scores, everyone else at the table grimly begins the next step: rubbing their foreheads about ways to get those test scores up.

What to do, what to do? Required summer school for low achievers? Special classes? Day off for everyone for better scores?

But alas, none of these suggestions will fly. They are either too complicated, too expensive, or too . . . too something. Finally, a plain-spoken member of the group relieves the tension by saying what needs to be said: "You know, it's those kids at the bottom—the lower fifth, or so. They are the ones who keep pulling the overall scores down. Those are the hardest scores to raise."

Exactly. The problem isn't the students who try their best on tests and meet or exceed state averages. It's not even the ones who don't do so well but who are willing to try harder. It's the ones who show up late for the test, complain, fill in any dots for a few minutes, then put their heads down and snore.

Why are they in school? Why must they be allowed to jeopardize the school's test scores, create most of the disciplinary problems, even reduce the quality of instruction for motivated kids?

Simple—compulsory attendance laws. Compulsory attendance laws are laws that say kids must be in school.

But compulsory attendance laws also force many students who are hostile, have little desire to learn, and play the fool five days a week to attend school.

The irony is that compulsory attendance laws don't even make kids go to school in the first place. In fact, a study by two economists, William Landes and Lewis Solomon, found little evidence that compulsory attendance laws increased rates of attendance at all. Compulsory attendance just recognizes what's already happening: almost all kids go to school because they want to. (Sound unbelievable? You can get almost any student upset by seriously suggesting he quit school. Try it.) Compulsory attendance is not the motivator that fills the classrooms.

So you might wonder what's the harm in having compulsory attendance, if only in principle?

First, schools must try to enforce compulsory attendance because it's the law. But they can't do a good job of it because of the expense involved. When was the last time you heard of a child being hauled into school by a truancy officer? Schools don't have the money. Instead, schools must rely on deans, counselors, and assistant principals to plead with poor attendees, threaten them with punishments, suspend them, and even send them to specially-created (and costly) Saturday classes.

GO →

Compulsory Attendance Laws—Get Rid of 'Em *(cont.)*

But why is that done? Kids who don't go to school regularly also don't do homework, don't learn much of value, and defy the school to do anything about it. After all, they know that they have to be in school, right? It's the law. All they have to do is hang on until graduation, because most schools will graduate students who do the barest minimum.

"What're you gonna do, Mr. or Ms. Principal—kick me out?"

Sure, why not? Imagine public schools being able to tell poor attendees, who are almost always failing, too, "You're done. You're expelled. You don't belong here."

There are schools that do it. They're private. And the ability to toss out students who don't want the education contributes enormously to positive school climate. How long do you think it would it be before poor attendees, troublemakers, and class clowns at a public school changed their ways once it became clear there was no compulsory attendance safety net under them? It's not like they couldn't go to school somewhere else. But this time, they'd have to pay tuition.

How many kids getting kicked out are we really talking about? In large urban areas, approximately 15 percent of the school-age children are almost permanently absent from school. In suburban areas, the figure is probably a lot less. And you can bet on this: the number of students skipping school or causing trouble when they are in attendance would be almost zero.

It would be better if they knew that there was no such thing as compulsory attendance, and public schools were not required to make them attend in the first place.

➢ STOP ➣

Directions: Choose the correct answer for each question.

Part I—The Dewey Decimal System

Libraries in the United States use the system devised by Melvil Dewey in 1876. This method is usually called "The Dewey Decimal System." Dewey's system classifies knowledge in ten general areas and assigns numbers to each.

The Dewey Decimal System

000–099—General Knowledge
100–199—Philosophy
200–299—Religion
300–399—Social Sciences
400–499—Language
500–599—Pure Science
600–699—Applied Science
700–799—The Arts
800–899—Literature
900–999—History and Travel

1. In which area of the library would you find the book, *Religions of the World*?
   (A) 100–199
   (B) 200–299
   (C) 700–799
   (D) 800–899

2. In which area of the library would you find the book, *Life in Ancient Rome*?
   (F) 200–299
   (G) 700–799
   (H) 900–999
   (J) 400–499

3. You're doing a report on the life of Maya Angelou, the poet and author. You need a copy of *I Know Why the Caged Bird Sings*. In which section of the library would you find it?
   (A) 000–099
   (B) 700–799
   (C) 800–899
   (D) 200–299

4. Your Spanish class is going to Mexico. Your assignment is to research the history of Mexico City. In which section of the library would you look?
   (F) 400–499
   (G) 700–799
   (H) 100–199
   (J) 900–999

GO →

Part II—Library Terms

5. A group of letters and numbers, given to books in the library so they can be arranged easily.

   (A) index (B) call number (C) title (D) catalog

6. A list of books or journal articles, usually appearing at the end of a researched piece of writing.

   (F) index (G) table of contents (H) bibliography (J) table

7. A reference book published each year containing various facts. It is useful for locating brief information about people, places, events, and statistical data.

   (A) atlas (B) encyclopedia (C) annual magazine (D) almanac

8. Written information about a book or journal article. A complete one includes information such as author, page numbers, volume number, and publication date.

   (F) citation (G) copyright (H) introduction (J) headline

9. A summary, usually of an article, highlighting all the key ideas in the article.

   (A) plot (B) abstract (C) obituary (D) web site

10. A book about someone written by someone else.

    (F) history (G) fanzine (H) biography (J) profile

11. A book composed of an alphabetical listing of words with their meanings.

    (A) atlas (B) thesaurus (C) dictionary (D) owner's manual

12. A magazine published by an institution or group, such the American Medical Association. It is more scholarly than magazines found at newsstands.

    (F) pamphlet (G) booklet (H) tip sheet (J) journal

13. A reference book, either general or about a specific field, that provides background information and facts, such as *World Book* or *Encarta*.

    (A) summary (B) textbook (C) dictionary (D) encyclopedia

14. The story of someone's life, as written by that person.

    (F) autobiography (G) bibliography (H) biography (J) genealogy

15. The shelves where books, either reference or circulating, are located.

    (A) vault (B) racks (C) reference (D) stacks

GO →

Part III—Online/CD-ROM Searching

Nearly all libraries offer a computerized catalog and searches on CD-ROM databases. Where might you search for each of the following topics?

16. How the NCAA has responded to incidents of gambling among players

(F) newspaper index (G) journal index (H) online book catalog

17. Medical experiments in the treatment of AIDS

(A) newspaper index (B) journal index (C) online book catalog

18. The history of space exploration

(F) newspaper index (G) journal index (H) online book catalog

19. The President's recent remarks about China

(A) newspaper index (B) journal index (C) online book catalog

20. Galileo: his conflict with the Church over his theories

(F) newspaper index (G) journal index (H) online book catalog

Part IV—Research Paper Terms

Below is an index of terms in a book called *How to Write a Research Report.*

(A)	Bibliography 9, 25, 26	(F)	Editing 24
(B)	Charts 7	(G)	Endnotes 10, 25, 26
(C)	Conclusions 23	(H)	Fair use 11
(D)	Drafting 20, 21	(J)	Captions 15, 16

21. Where would you find information about writing the ending of your research report?
22. Where would you find example of improving what you've written by making changes?
23. Where would you find information about how to list the books and articles you've used at the end of your report?

(A)	Note-taking 6, 18, 20	(F)	Library research 35, 36
(B)	Interview 5	(G)	Manuscript form 26
(C)	Introductions 21	(H)	Graphs 7
(D)	Library resources 2, 3, 4	(J)	Outlining 19, 20, 26

24. Where would you find information about the right way to paragraph and space the writing in your report?
25. Where would you find information about writing down ideas and facts you borrowed from books, magazines, and articles?
26. Where would you find information about how to plan your report so all the ideas flowed logically?

➢ **STOP** ➢

Introduction

To perform your best on the mathematics section of a standardized test, you need not know the right answer every time. But you do need to use two important strategies that will improve your score: *estimating* and *recognizing a reasonable answer*.

Here's the Idea

Estimating is a way of getting close to a right answer by rounding. When you round numbers in a problem, you will get an answer that is close to the right answer.

Recognizing a reasonable answer means deciding that an answer choice is probably right, based on what you already know about numbers and problems. You can drop some answer choices right away because they are not reasonable.

However, before we look at these two skills, below are some tips that apply to taking any test, whether it is in language arts, math, science, social studies, fine arts, or computers and technology. These tips will be repeated because they are important!

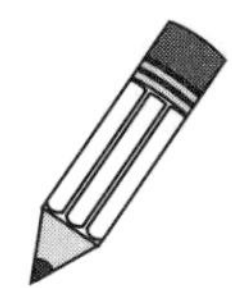

Test-Taking Tips

- **Read directions carefully before marking any test questions,** even though you have done that kind of test before. You may think you already know what the directions say, but don't ignore them—read them over. If you don't understand the directions, raise your hand and ask for help. Although your teacher must read the directions exactly as they are written, the teacher can make sure you understand what the directions mean.
- **Follow instructions.** Pay close attention to the sample exercises. They will help you understand what the items on the test will be like and how to mark your answer sheet properly.
- **Read the entire question and all the answer choices.** Do not stop reading when you have found a correct answer. Choices D or E may read "B and D" or "all of the above." On some tests, two answers are both correct or possibly none of the answers is correct. You need to read all the answer choices before marking your answer.
- **And remember—taking a test is not a race!** There are no prizes for finishing first. Use all of the time provided for the test. If you have time left over, check your answers.

Try and Discuss

Now let's discuss those two skills for mathematics tests—*estimating* and *recognizing a reasonable answer.* When you estimate, you use round numbers to come close to the correct answer without even working through the problem. Use these two rules for rounding:

- Round up for numbers five and greater than five.
- Round down for numbers less than five.

Immigrants to the United States, 1976–1986

Country of Origin	Approximate Numbers
Mexico	720,000
Vietnam	425,000
Philippines	379,000
Korea	363,000

SOURCE: Foner, Eric and John A. Garrity, eds. *The Reader's Companion to American History* (Boston: Houghton Mifflin, 1991) 538.

How many fewer immigrants came from Vietnam than Mexico?

(A) 220,250 (B) 120,250
(C) 295,000 (D) 350,000

Fill in the correct circle.

Ⓐ Ⓑ Ⓒ Ⓓ

If you round down 720,000 to 700,000 and round down 425,000 to 400,000, you can do the subtraction in your head: 300,000. Which answer comes closest? The answer is (C) 295,000. Estimating works well when you don't know the answer or you're trying to go faster on a test because time is short.

Now, what about recognizing a reasonable answer? Reasonable means "likely based on careful thinking."

$$\begin{array}{r} 200 \\ \underline{\text{x } .4} \end{array}$$

(F) 800 (H) 80
(G) 60 (J) 20

Fill in the correct circle.

Ⓕ Ⓖ Ⓗ Ⓙ

For instance, if you saw this problem, you would know that (F) 800 is clearly not a reasonable answer. Two hundred is being multiplied by a decimal. (G) 60 is far less than half of 200, and 200 is being multiplied by .4 not .5. And (J) 20 is 10 percent of 200. You know these things already.

Recognizing a reasonable answer is a powerful strategy when you want to eliminate answers. In other words, you can drop some answer choices immediately because they are not reasonable. Don't bother with answer choices that are clearly wrong because they are unreasonable. This improves your chances of choosing the correct answer, even if you have difficulty doing the problem.

Tips That Help

Remember the following:

- Use *estimating* to come close to the correct answer.
- Learn to *recognize a reasonable answer* so you can eliminate choices that are clearly wrong.

Now try the practice tests, listening to your teacher's directions.

Mathematics: Rational and Irrational Numbers

Directions: Choose whether the number is rational or irrational.

1. $\sqrt{5}$

   (A) irrational

   (B) rational

2. $-\sqrt{25}$

   (A) irrational

   (B) rational

3. $-\frac{3}{4}$

   (A) irrational

   (B) rational

4. $3\frac{1}{7}$

   (A) irrational

   (B) rational

5. 0.0031

   (A) irrational

   (B) rational

6. 6.51

   (A) irrational

   (B) rational

Directions: Find the square root. Give the answer in the simplest form.

7. $\sqrt{\frac{25}{49}}$

   (A) 7/5 (C) 5/7

   (B) 35 (D) 24

8. $\sqrt{\frac{1}{121}}$

   (F) 1/11 (H) 1.10

   (G) 11/1 (J) 121

9. $\sqrt{\frac{4}{9}}$

   (A) 5 (C) 3/2

   (B) .25 (D) 2/3

10. $\sqrt{\frac{9}{144}}$

    (F) 3/9 (H) 1/4

    (G) 2/12 (J) 133

11. $\sqrt{\frac{100}{16}}$

    (A) 5/2 (C) 94

    (B) 25/8 (D) 32

12. $\sqrt{\frac{4}{25}}$

    (F) 2/12.5 (H) –19

    (G) 19 (J) 2/5

➤ **STOP** ➤

Directions: Find the sum.

1. –5 + (–5)
   (A) 0
   (B) 5
   (C) –10
   (D) –25

2. –43 + 51
   (F) 8
   (G) 92
   (H) –8
   (J) –92

3. –8 + (–6)
   (A) –48
   (B) 2
   (C) –2
   (D) –14

4. 40 + (–29)
   (F) –11
   (G) 11
   (H) –69
   (J) 69

5. –32 + 32
   (A) –64
   (B) 64
   (C) 0
   (D) 32/32

6. 15 + (–9)
   (F) –24
   (G) 24
   (H) 6
   (J) –6

Directions: Find each difference.

7. –11– 8
   (A) 19
   (B) –19
   (C) 3
   (D) –3

8. –8 – 22
   (F) 30
   (G) 14
   (H) –30
   (J) 14

9. –8 – (–26)
   (A) 18
   (B) –34
   (C) –18
   (D) 34

10. –30 – (–24)
    (F) –54
    (G) 6
    (H) –6
    (J) 54

11. –62 – 41
    (A) 21
    (B) –21
    (C) 103
    (D) –103

12. 22 – (–17)
    (F) 39
    (G) –39
    (H) 5
    (J) –5

GO →

Directions: Find each product or quotient.

13. 12 (–7)
   (A) 84
   (B) –84
   (C) –5
   (D) 5

14. 15 (20)
   (F) –300
   (G) 35
   (H) 300
   (J) –35

15. 42 (–3)
   (A) 39
   (B) –45
   (C) –39
   (D) –126

16. 22 (–5)
   (F) –110
   (G) –17
   (H) 27
   (J) –27

17. –125 ÷ (–5)
   (A) –25
   (B) –130
   (C) 130
   (D) 25

18. 96 ÷ (–24)
   (F) 72
   (G) –4
   (H) –72
   (J) 120

19. (–25) (–40)
   (A) 65
   (B) –65
   (C) 1000
   (D) 115

20. (–32) (9)
   (F) 2
   (G) –288
   (H) –23
   (J) 41

21. 64 ÷ (–4)
   (A) –16
   (B) 60
   (C) 16
   (D) 18

22. 30 ÷ 6
   (F) –5
   (G) 24
   (H) 5
   (J) 36

23. –105 ÷ (–7)
   (A) –15
   (B) –112
   (C) 15
   (D) 112

➢ **STOP** ➣

Mathematics: Real Numbers Part II

Directions: Fill in the circle of the correct answer.

Write each fraction or mixed number as a decimal.

1. 6/8
   (A) 0.63 (C) 0.58
   (B) 0.75 (D) .058

2. 1 5/8
   (F) 1.347 (H) 1.625
   (G) 2.70 (J) 2.015

3. 5 37/50
   (A) 513.0 (C) 237.50
   (B) 5.74 (D) 6.13

Write each fraction or mixed number in simplest form.

4. 6 7/14
   (F) 6 1/2 (H) 67/14
   (G) 42/14 (J) 13/14

5. 64/72
   (A) 1 8/72 (C) 8/9
   (B) 1 8/9 (D) 12/9

6. 3/18
   (F) 6/3 (H) 3/9
   (G) 1/6 (J) 1/3

Write each fraction or mixed number as a percent.

7. 5 3/4
   (A) 534% (C) 575%
   (B) 53.4% (D) 203%

8. 45/50
   (F) 90% (H) 5%
   (G) 95% (J) 53.4%

9. 1/3
   (A) 30% (C) 300%
   (B) 30.3% (D) 33.3%

Write each percent as a decimal.

10. 33%
    (F) 33.0 (H) 33.3
    (G) 0.33 (J) 330

11. 115%
    (A) 11.5 (C) 110.5
    (B) 115 (D) 1.15

12. 234%
    (F) 2.34 (H) .234
    (G) 23.4 (J) 23.40

Write each percent as a fraction or mixed number in simplest form.

13. 99%
    (A) 99/1 (C) 99/100
    (B) 99.1 (D) 990

14. 12 1/2%
    (F) 1/8 (H) 1/144
    (G) 1/12 (J) 1/6

15. 3%
    (A) 30/100 (C) 3/100
    (B) 3/10 (D) 30/10

GO →

Directions: Fill in the circle of the correct answer.

Which proportion can be used to answer the question?

16. 32 is 12 percent of what number?
    (F) 32/12 = *n*/100
    (G) *n*/32 = 12/100
    (H) 32/*n* = 12/100
    (J) 100/*n* = 12/32

17. 81 is 90 percent of what number?
    (A) *n*/81 = 90/100
    (B) 81/*n* = 90/100
    (C) 90/81 = *n*/100
    (D) 100/81 = *n*/90

18. What percent of 60 is 28?
    (F) 28/60 = *n*/100
    (G) 60/100 = *n*/28
    (H) 100/*n* = 28/60
    (J) 28/100 = 60/*n*

19. 5 percent of 38 is what number?
    (A) 5/*n* = 38/100
    (B) *n*/38 = 100/5
    (C) *n*/38 = 5/100
    (D) 38/100 = *n*/5

20. What number is 47 percent of 19?
    (F) *n*/47 = 19/100
    (G) 19/*n* = 100/47
    (H) *n*/19 = 47/100
    (J) 19/47 = *n*/100

Find each number or percent.

21. What number is 50 percent of 19?
    (A) 8
    (B) 9.5
    (C) 190
    (D) 27

22. 50 is 80 percent of what number?
    (F) 625
    (G) 6.25
    (H) 62.5
    (J) 400

23. 54 is 3 percent of what number?
    (A) 180
    (B) 1800
    (C) 162
    (D) 1620

24. 45 is what percent of 60?
    (F) 75 percent
    (G) 7.5 percent
    (H) 80 percent
    (J) 15 percent

25. 100 is what percent of 50?
    (A) 50 percent
    (B) 150 percent
    (C) 200 percent
    (D) .5 percent

26. 150 percent of 60 is what number?
    (F) 20
    (G) 90
    (H) 18
    (J) 36

27. 75 is what percent of 60?
    (A) 52 percent
    (B) 115 percent
    (C) 125 percent
    (D) 90 percent

GO →

28. The sales tax in France is 6.5 percent. How much tax will you pay for a souvenir of the Eiffel tower if it costs $20?

(F) $1.30

(G) $18

(H) $4.50

(J) $1.80

29. A long cab ride from O'Hare airport in Chicago to Homewood, Illinois, was $30 including a tip of 20 percent. What was the cost of the trip without the tip?

(A) $24

(B) $22

(C) $25

(D) $36

Is each proportion TRUE or FALSE?

30. 3/5 = 4/6

(A) True (B) False

31. 12/3 = 16/5

(A) True (B) False

32. 12/8 = 13/9

(A) True (B) False

33. 25/3 = 100/12

(A) True (B) False

34. 13/39 = 7/21

(A) True (B) False

35. 0.5/8 = 3/48

(A) True (B) False

Solve each proportion.

36. $10/40 = 7/y$

(F) $y = 1.75$

(G) $y = 280$

(H) $y = 28$

(J) $y = .25$

37. $0.6/5 = 1.2/x$

(A) $x = 10$

(B) $x = .0114$

(C) $x = 6$

(D) $x = .072$

38. $16/k = 3/9$

(F) $k = 144$

(G) $k = 16$

(H) $k = .33$

(J) $k = 48$

39. $35/3.5 = z/2$

(A) $z = 10$

(B) $z = 7$

(C) $z = 20$

(D) $z = 70$

40. $3/19 = 6/w$

(F) $w = .157$

(G) $w = 38$

(H) $w = 114$

(J) $w = 18$

➢ STOP ➣

Directions: Match the terms on the left with the definitions on the right.

1. polygon
2. sides of a polygon
3. vertex of a polygon
4. diagonal of a polygon
5. congruent
6. regular polygon
7. parallelogram
8. rectangle

(A) having the same size and shape
(B) a point where two sides of the polygon meet
(C) a plane figure formed by line segments, each intersecting exactly two other sides, one at each endpoint
(D) a polygon with two pairs of parallel and congruent sides
(F) a line segment that joins two nonconsecutive vertices of the polygon
(G) a polygon with two pairs of congruent and parallel sides and four right angles
(H) the line segments that form a polygon
(J) a polygon in which all of the sides are congruent and all of the angles are congruent

---

Directions: Choose the correct answer to each question.

9. Find the perimeter.

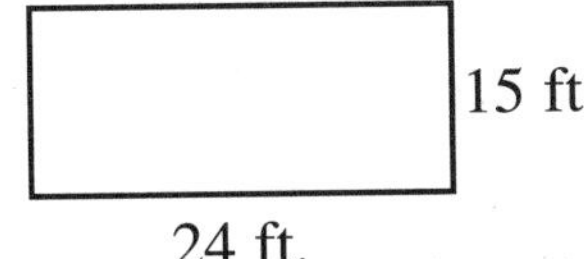

(A) 72 feet
(B) 39 feet
(C) 78 feet
(D) 64 feet

10. Find the perimeter.

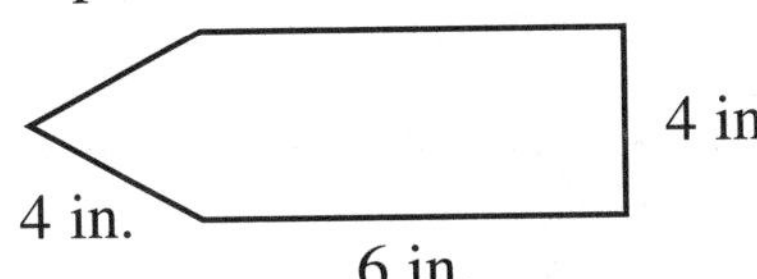

(F) 26.4 inches
(G) 24 inches
(H) 48 inches
(J) 26 inches

11. Find the area.

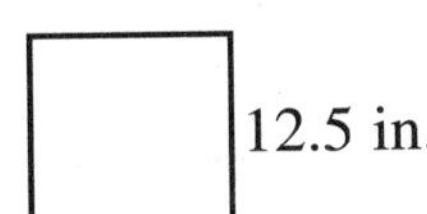

(A) 50 in.
(B) 156.25 in.^{2}
(C) 145 in.
(D) 125 in.^{2}

12. Find the area.

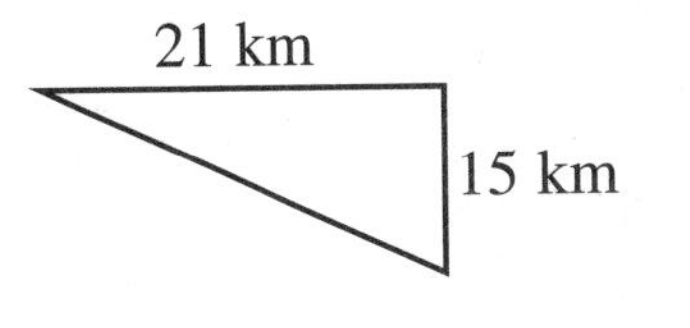

(F) 157.5 km
(G) 57 km
(H) 1.57 km
(J) none of these

13. The diameter of the circle is 12 inches. Find the area. Use 3.14 for π.

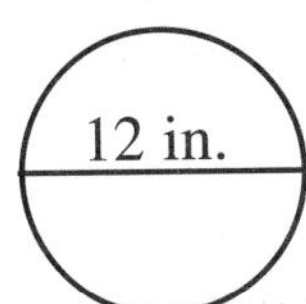

(A) 107 inches
(B) 113 in.^{2}
(C) 3.14 (12)
(D) 12/3.14

14. The radius of the circle is 28 inches. Find the circumference. Use 22/7 for π.

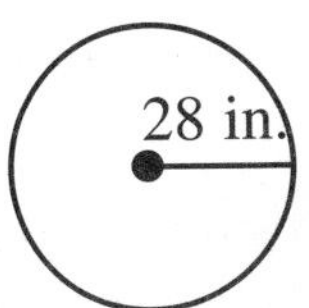

(F) 170 inches
(G) 176 inches
(H) 74.5 inches
(J) 58.7 inches

STOP

Directions: Choose the correct answer to each question.

1. Simplify: $3x + 7x + x$
   (A) 10x2
   (B) $10 + 3x$
   (C) $11x$
   (D) none of these

2. State the expression without parentheses: $4(5 - 4m)$
   (F) $20 - 16m$
   (G) $4m$
   (H) $4(1m)$
   (J) $-20\ m$

3. $7y + 6 = 20$
   (A) 3
   (B) 2
   (C) 1.25
   (D) $2y$

4. Subtract: $\begin{array}{r} 5n + 1 \\ \underline{-\ (2n - 5)} \end{array}$
   (F) $3n + 4$
   (G) $3n + 6$
   (H) $7n + 4$
   (J) none of these

Find the greatest common factor of each pair.

5. 10, 12
   (A) 5
   (B) 6
   (C) 2
   (D) 4

6. 16, 72
   (F) 2
   (G) 8
   (H) 12
   (J) 16

7. 12, 18
   (A) 4
   (B) 3
   (C) 6
   (D) 18

Factor the following problems.

8. $y^2 + 14y + 49$
   (F) 2
   (G) $(y + 7)^2$
   (H) 7^2
   (J) none of these

9. $n^2 + 20n + 64$
   (A) 4
   (B) 4^2
   (C) $(n + 4^2)$
   (D) $(n + 16)(n + 4)$

10. $x^2 + 5x - 14$
   (F) 3^2
   (G) $(x - 9)$
   (H) $(x + 7)(x - 2)$
   (J) $(3 - 9^2)\ 2$

➢ STOP ➣

Science Strategies

Introduction

Science tries to uncover the physical truth about the way things work—how the seasons change, why animals hibernate, or what kinds of rock are created by volcanoes, for example. To perform your best on questions about science, you must pay attention to important words in each question that might make the answer choices true or untrue.

Here's the Idea

People who work in science try to find out what is true and what is untrue. Questions on science tests often have words in them, such as *not, but, except, always, never,* and *only,* which make answer choices true or untrue. You must watch for these key words in the test questions.

However, before we look at these key words, below are some tips that apply to taking any test, whether it is in language arts, mathematics, science, social studies, fine arts, or computers and technology. These tips will be repeated because they are important!

Test-Taking Tips

- **Read directions carefully before marking any test questions**, even though you have done that kind of test before. You may think you already know what the directions say, but don't ignore them—read them over. If you don't understand the directions, raise your hand and ask for help. Although your teacher must read the directions exactly as they are written, the teacher can make sure you understand what the directions mean.
- **Follow instructions.** Pay close attention to the sample exercises. They will help you understand what the items on the test will be like and how to mark your answer sheet properly.
- **Read the entire question and all the answer choices.** Do not stop reading when you have found a correct answer. Choices D or E may read "B and D" or "all of the above" or "none of the above." On some tests, two answers are both correct. You need to read all the answer choices before marking your answer.
- **For long reading passages, read the questions first so you know what to look for.** If you read the questions first, you'll find information in the passage that answers questions.
- **Remember that taking a test is not a race!** There are no prizes for finishing first. Use all of the time provided for the test. If you have time left over, check your answers.

Try and Discuss

Let's discuss those key words in many science questions: *not, but, except, always, never*, and *only*. Words such as *not, but, except, always, never,* and *only* make a big difference, but you must be alert for them. Look at these questions.

Which of the following is *not* part of the circulatory system?

(A) heart

(B) bones

(C) blood vessels

(D) blood

Fill in the correct circle.

Ⓐ Ⓑ Ⓒ Ⓓ

At first glance, "blood" might seem like the odd one here because it is a liquid; it is not a solid object like the others. But read the question carefully: "Which of the following is *not* part of the circulatory system?" It's not asking "Which one does not belong?" The circulatory system does not include bones, so (B) "bones" is the correct answer.

Now look at the following question:

Which of the following is *not* an example of fungi?

(A) mold

(B) mushrooms

(C) mildew

(D) dirt

Fill in the correct circle.

Ⓐ Ⓑ Ⓒ Ⓓ

Mold, mildew, and dirt all seem like unpleasant things at first glance. So you might think, as you let your eye go over the list, that "mushroom" is the odd one here—at least you can eat mushrooms pretty regularly. But look closely at the question: "Which of the following is *not* an example of fungi?" Mushrooms, mildew, and mold are all part of one group—they are all fungi. Dirt is the odd one—it is not a fungus. A lot depends on that part of the question, "*not* an example of fungi."

Tips That Help

Remember the following:

- People who work in science try to find out what is true and untrue.
- Pay attention to key words in science questions, such as *not, but, except, always, never*, and *only,* that will make answer choices true or untrue.

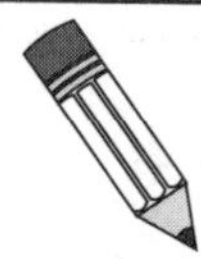

Now try the practice tests, listening to your teacher's directions.

Directions: Choose the correct answer to each question.

1. Biology is the scientific study of
   (A) insects and animals.
   (B) human processes.
   (C) living things.
   (D) cells.

2. Which is NOT a characteristic of a living thing?
   (F) the ability to reproduce
   (G) the ability to communicate
   (H) the ability to grow
   (J) the ability to respond to changes in the environment.

3. Which is NOT part of the nervous system of creatures with backbones?
   (A) the brain
   (B) the heart
   (C) the spinal cord
   (D) the nerves

4. The nervous system is made up of billions of special cells called
   (F) neurons. (H) electrons.
   (G) protons. (J) neutrinos.

5. Nerve messages are known as
   (A) impulses. (C) jolts.
   (B) shocks. (D) thoughts.

6. Which is NOT part of the nervous system?
   (F) the central nervous system
   (G) the peripheral nervous system
   (H) the autonomic nervous system
   (J) the pathway nervous system

7. Which is NOT a part of the brain?
   (A) the cerebrum (C) the aorta
   (B) the cerebellum (D) the brain stem

8. Which is NOT a brain function?
   (F) coordinating muscle movement
   (G) creating speech
   (H) maintaining heartbeat
   (J) encouraging better running

True or False

9. The brain stem is connected to the spinal cord at the base of the skull.
   (A) True
   (B) False

10. The backbone, not the spinal cord, carries messages to and from the brain.
    (A) True
    (B) False

11. Ganglia are clusters of neurons outside the central nervous system.
    (A) True
    (B) False

12. The places where one neuron communicates with another is called a synapse.
    (A) True
    (B) False

13. Learning how to ride a bike is an example of a reflex.
    (A) True
    (B) False

14. An example of a disorder of the nervous system is a stroke.
    (A) True
    (B) False

GO →

15. Which is NOT part of a seed?
    (A) embryo
    (B) root
    (C) stored food
    (D) protective coating

16. Which is NOT an example of an angiosperm?
    (F) shrubs
    (G) leafy trees
    (H) cone-bearing trees
    (J) soft-stemmed plants

17. Which is NOT an example of an enclosed seed?
    (A) corn kernel
    (B) a cutting taken from a plant
    (C) an apple
    (D) a pea pod

18. Which is NOT part of a plant's reproductive system?
    (F) fallopian tube
    (G) pistil
    (H) stamen
    (J) anther

19. Seeds are spread by
    (A) wind.
    (B) people.
    (C) water.
    (D) all of these.

20. What do seeds NOT require to germinate?
    (F) water
    (G) oxygen
    (H) right temperature
    (J) sunlight

True or False

21. Coconuts are fruits, not seeds.
    (A) True
    (B) False

22. The bigger the seed, the bigger the plant.
    (A) True
    (B) False

23. The seeds of plants are the same size.
    (A) True
    (B) False

24. Pine cones are seeds.
    (A) True
    (B) False

25. Seed formation results from sexual reproduction, in which a sperm (male sex cell) unites with an egg (female sex cell).
    (A) True
    (B) False

26. Bees prevent pollination.
    (A) True
    (B) False

27. Ripe seeds sprout through a process called germination.
    (A) True
    (B) False

28. Many seeds remain dormant during the cold winter months.
    (A) True
    (B) False

GO →

29. Respiration in plants is taking in of carbon dioxide and giving off oxygen.
    (A) True (B) False

30. Heredity is the passing on of biological traits from one __________ to the next.
    (F) person (H) race
    (G) generation (J) owner

31. Tiny structures inside each cell called ______ carry traits.
    (A) ovaries (C) genes
    (B) threads (D) blood

32. Long chains of DNA in structures are called
    (F) chromosomes.
    (G) traits.
    (H) ladders.
    (J) color codes.

33. Which would NOT be an example of heredity?
    (A) You can run fast.
    (B) You can play a difficult piece on the piano.
    (C) You have blue eyes.
    (D) You know how to repair a VCR.

34. Chromosomes are found in the part of a cell known as the
    (F) cytoplasm. (H) nucleus.
    (G) membrane. (J) mitosis.

True or False

35. Chromosomes are never paired.
    (A) True (B) False

36. The uniting of an egg cell and a sperm cell is called fertilization.
    (A) True (B) False

37. Asexual reproduction involves two parents.
    (A) True (B) False

38. After the egg has been fertilized, it begins to divide and produce exact copies of itself by a type of cell division called mitosis.
    (A) True (B) False

GO →

Matching

39. zoology	(A) study of plants
40. botany	(B) study of animals
41. biology	(C) study of the structure of living things
42. anatomy	(D) study of living things

43. ecology	(F) study of life functions such as digestion
44. genetics	(G) study of heredity
45. physiology	(H) study of relationships between living things
46. psychology	(J) study of the mind and behavior

47. marine biology	(A) study of organisms under a microscope
48. ornithology	(B) study of birds
49. embryology	(C) study of how plants and animals form
50. microbiology	(D) study of life in the ocean

51. dominant	(F) one of more abnormal genes from parents
52. recessive	(G) tends to occur more often
53. hereditary disorders	(H) permanent change in the DNA
54. mutation	(J) tends not to occur

55. natural selection	(A) genetic makeup of a trait
56. gene pool	(B) building blocks for cells
57. genotype	(C) genes of all the individuals in a population
58. proteins	(D) gradual improvement in the species

➢ **STOP** ≺

Directions: Choose the correct answer to each question.

1. The most basic chemical substances are the chemical
   (A) parts. (C) elements.
   (B) behaviors. (D) blocks.

2. Each chemical element is made up of only one kind of
   (F) atom. (H) ring.
   (G) molecule. (J) nature.

3. Chemists use letters of the alphabet as __________ for the elements.
   (A) signs (C) names
   (B) symbols (D) numbers

4. Carbon, hydrogen, oxygen, and iron are
   (F) Ca, Hy, Ox, Fe.
   (G) C, Hy, O, Ir.
   (H) C, H, O, and Fe.
   (J) Ca, Hy, O, Ir.

5. Electrical forces at the atomic level create chemical ________ that join two or more atoms together, forming _________.
   (A) rings/electrons
   (B) bonds/molecules
   (C) elements/molecules
   (D) atoms/symbols

6. When atoms of two or more different elements bond together, they form a chemical
   (F) mixture. (H) solution.
   (G) atom. (J) compound.

7. A new substance that is man-made from natural materials is called
   (A) rare.
   (B) an isotope.
   (C) synthetic.
   (D) plastic.

8. Each officially named ________ has a chemical symbol consisting of one or two letters.
   (F) atom (H) compound
   (G) element (J) molecule

9. The periodic table lists the elements in rows, called periods, in order of increasing _________ number.
   (A) atomic (C) molecular
   (B) chemical (D) big

10. What does the periodic table NOT include?
    (F) atomic mass numbers
    (G) atomic weights
    (H) numbers of electrons in electron shells
    (J) size of atoms

11. Atomic number is the number of __________ (positively charged particles) in an atom's nucleus.
    (A) electrons (C) protons
    (B) nuclei (D) quarks

12. When wood burns, matter changes into
    (F) a gas. (H) particles.
    (G) energy. (J) none of the above.

13. Substances that can be broken down by chemical change into simpler elements are called
    (A) mixtures. (C) compounds.
    (B) chemicals. (D) crystals.

14. Most of the compounds found in living organisms contain the element
    (F) water. (H) plasma.
    (G) carbon. (J) chlorophyll.

GO →

True or False

15. All the atoms of an element have the same number of protons.
    (A) True (B) False

16. All atoms, except those of the simplest form of hydrogen, also have particles with no electric charge, called neutrons, in their nucleus.
    (A) True (B) False

17. Atomic mass number is the total number of protons and neutrons in an isotope.
    (A) True (B) False

18. All atoms have four or more electrons surrounding the nucleus.
    (A) True (B) False

19. The electrons are arranged in levels called the electron solar system, according to how much energy the electrons have.
    (A) True (B) False

20. Molecules are made up of electrons held together in certain arrangements.
    (A) True (B) False

21. Scientists use chemical formulas to show the composition of molecules.
    (A) True (B) False

22. Atoms link together in molecules through strong attractive forces called charges.
    (A) True (B) False

Matching

Directions: Choose either solid, liquid, or gas for each question.

23. atoms arranged in regular patterns
24. does not change shape easily
25. exerts pressure equally in all directions
26. has form
27. has low densities
28. has the ability to flow
29. has no shape of its own
30. takes the shape of any container in which it is placed

(A) a solid
(B) a liquid
(C) a gas

➢ STOP ➢

Directions: Choose the correct answer for each question.

Magnetism and Electricity

1. Which is NOT true of magnetism?
   (A) Magnetism is a force.
   (B) Magnetism may exist in certain natural materials.
   (C) Magnetism may be produced by electric current flowing through a coil of wire.
   (D) Magnetism adds to the weight of objects.

2. Which is NOT a use of magnets?
   (F) fasteners and latches
   (G) tools, appliances, and trains
   (H) making planes fly
   (J) audiotape and videotape

3. Which is NOT correct?
   (A) Some rocks, minerals, and meteorites are natural magnets.
   (B) The earth itself is a giant magnet.
   (C) The sun is a magnet.
   (D) Clouds travel by magnetic force.

4. Which is NOT correct?
   (F) A bar magnet hung by a string will turn until one end points north and the other end points south.
   (G) There is a north and south pole.
   (H) There is an east and west pole.
   (J) If a magnet is broken or cut in half, each piece has a north and south magnetic pole.

True or False

5. Magnetism causes unlike magnetic poles to attract each other, but like poles to repel each other.
   (A) True (B) False

6. If the north pole of a magnet is brought near the south pole of another magnet, the magnetic force pushes the magnets apart.
   (A) True (B) False

7. The area around a magnet where the force of magnetism can be felt is a magnetic field.
   (A) True (B) False

8. You can see a magnetic field in the air.
   (A) True (B) False

9. The needle of a magnetic compass, for example, is actually a magnet.
   (A) True (B) False

10. Which will a magnet NOT attract?
    (F) iron
    (H) nickel
    (G) steel
    (J) cotton

11. A(n) _________ is a type of magnet produced by an electric current.
    (A) compass
    (B) electromagnet
    (C) transformer
    (D) light bulb

12. Which is NOT correct?
    (F) Each proton carries one unit of positive electric charge.
    (G) Each molecule has a positive charge.
    (H) Each electron carries one unit of negative charge.
    (J) Neutrons have no charge.

GO →

Matching

(A) Ampere
(B) Ohm
(C) Electric circuit
(D) Electromagnetism
(F) Electron
(G) Conductor
(H) Electric current
(J) Iron filings

13. __________ is the unit used to measure the rate of flow of an electric current.
14. __________ is a material through which electric current flows easily.
15. __________ is the path that an electric current follows.
16. __________ is the flow of electric charges.
17. __________ is a basic force in the universe that involves both electricity and magnetism.
18. __________ is a subatomic particle with a negative electric charge. Insulator is a material that opposes the flow of electric current.
19. __________ is the unit used to measure a material's resistance to the flow of electric current.
20. __________ and a piece of paper can be used to show a magnetic field.

Sound

True or False

21. Acoustics is the science of sound and of its effects on people.

    (A) True (B) False

22. Pitch is the degree of highness or lowness of a sound as perceived by a listener.

    (A) True (B) False

23. The more rapidly an object vibrates, the lower will be the frequency.

    (A) True (B) False

24. Sound travels faster through liquids than it does through air.

    (A) True (B) False

25. The speed of sound is faster than the speed of light.

    (A) True (B) False

26. An echo is produced when the sound waves are absorbed into a hard surface.

    (A) True (B) False

27. A tuning fork making a piano string vibrate is called sympathetic vibration.

    (A) True (B) False

GO →

Light

28. All light comes from
    (F) atoms that have gained energy.
    (G) atomic activity.
    (H) heat.
    (J) colors.

29. Materials that glow in the dark like some watch faces are said to be
    (A) atomic. (C) exposed.
    (B) phosphorescent. (D) greenish.

30. The light emitted by fireflies is created by
    (F) heat. (H) reflected light.
    (G) chemicals. (J) radioactivity.

31. Light from the sun is a result of
    (A) reflection. (C) a nuclear reaction.
    (B) electricity. (D) pressure.

32. When high-speed particles from the sun hit molecules in the air, the shimmering light seen at night is called
    (F) a wave. (H) an aurora.
    (G) a sunset. (J) a burst.

Matching

(A) transparent (C) photoelectric (F) optics (H) translucent

(B) opaque (D) laser (G) prism (J) refraction

33. A _______ is a device that produces a powerful, narrow beam of light.
34. The study of light is called ________ .
35. A _________ material lets light rays pass through it unchanged.
36. A _________ material allows rays to pass through it, but not clearly.
37. An ________ material blocks all light.
38. A pencil looking bent in a glass of water is an example of _________.
39. A _________ cell is a device that turns light into electricity.
40. A _________ will separate light into colors.

➢ STOP ≺

Directions: Choose the correct answer for each question.

1. Geology is the study of the
   (A) land. (C) earthquakes.
   (B) solar system. (D) earth.

2. The earth probably was formed more than 4½ _____ years ago.
   (F) million (H) billion
   (G) thousand (J) hundred

3. Enormous land areas are raised by pressure and moved to create
   (A) seas. (C) deserts.
   (B) mountains. (D) tundra.

4. Hot melted rock called ______ flows from volcanoes.
   (F) molten (H) steel
   (G) lava (J) iron

5. Great rivers of ice called _______ slowly carved valleys, lakes, and river basins.
   (A) flows (C) glaciers
   (B) fjords (D) icebergs

6. One way of studying in rock what life on earth was like is to examine
   (F) coral. (H) shells.
   (G) fossils. (J) coal.

7. Geologists who study earthquakes believe the outer shell of Earth is made up of about 30
   (A) volcanoes. (C) plates.
   (B) feet. (D) cracks.

8. A volcano forms when
   (F) the surface of the earth is punctured.
   (G) man-made explosions crack the earth.
   (H) the floor of the ocean splits.
   (J) magma, hot gases, and fragments of rock burst through the surface.

9. Earthquakes usually occur where there are _____________ in the earth.
   (A) gases
   (B) faults
   (C) canyons
   (D) waves

10. Which would NOT be a fossil?
    (F) a plant
    (G) a skeleton
    (H) a tool
    (J) a shell

11. Most fossils are found in __________ rocks.
    (A) igneous
    (B) sedimentary
    (C) shell
    (D) ocean

12. Which could be the OLDEST fossils?
    (F) dinosaurs
    (G) invertebrates
    (H) sea bacteria
    (J) trees

13. The outer surface of Earth is called the
    (A) crust. (C) core.
    (B) mantle. (D) plate.

14. Which is NOT a way rock is formed?
    (F) lava cools and hardens
    (G) lightning strikes the ground
    (H) mud hardens
    (J) pressure and heat deep inside the earth changes one kind of rock into another

GO →

15. Which is NOT a kind of rock that makes up Earth's surface?
    (A) igneous
    (B) sedimentary
    (C) isotopic
    (D) metamorphic

16. Which of these changes Earth's surface?
    (F) weathering
    (G) erosion
    (H) changes in the crust
    (J) all of these

True or False

17. Everything that died long ago became a fossil.
    (A) True (B) False

18. A fossil of a fish found in a forest always means someone put it there.
    (A) True (B) False

19. Fossils show that no dinosaurs hatched from eggs.
    (A) True (B) False

20. Birds may be descended from flying lizards.
    (A) True (B) False

21. Older fossils are found near the surface of the earth; newer fossils are found deeper down.
    (A) True (B) False

22. Life on Earth began with dinosaurs.
    (A) True (B) False

23. Layers of fossils in rock show that living things became simpler over time.
    (A) True (B) False

➢ **STOP** ➣

Social Studies Strategies

Introduction

Social studies is all about people and places. It can be difficult at times to remember many names and events. But to perform your best on a social studies section, it helps to ask yourself a question about the question!

Here's the Idea

A social studies question may be about a region, a president, or an event. It helps focus your attention on what the question is asking—and it helps you eliminate choices, too—if you ask yourself *who, what, where, when*, or *how*.

However, before we look at these key words, below are some tips that apply to taking any test, whether it is in language arts, mathematics, science, social studies, fine arts, or computers and technology. These tips are repeated because they are important!

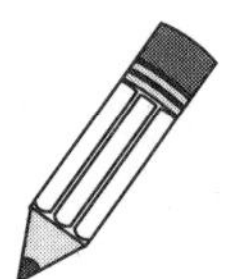

Test-Taking Tips

- **Read directions carefully before marking any test questions**, even though you have done that kind of test before. You may think you already know what the directions say, but don't ignore them—read them over. If you don't understand the directions, raise your hand and ask for help. Although your teacher must read the directions exactly as they are written, the teacher can make sure you understand what the directions mean.
- **Follow instructions.** Pay close attention to the sample exercises. They will help you understand what the items on the test will be like and how to mark your answer sheet properly.
- **Read the entire question and all the answer choices.** Do not stop reading when you have found a correct answer. Choices D or E may read "B and D" or "all of the above" or "none of the above." On some tests, two answers are both correct. You need to read all the answer choices before marking your answer.
- **For long reading passages, read the questions first so you know what to look for.** If you read the questions first, you'll find information in the passage that answers the questions.
- **Remember that taking a test is not a race!** There are no prizes for finishing first. Use all of the time provided for the test. If you have time left over, check your answers.

Try and Discuss

Let's discuss asking the questions *who, what, where, when*, or *how*. Social studies questions are about persons, places, or events and when or how they happened.

For example, here's a social studies test question:

A major industry of the Midwest region is

(A) agriculture.
(B) Illinois, Ohio, Wisconsin, Iowa, and Michigan.
(C) fishing.
(D) the Civil War.

Fill in the correct circle.

Ask yourself, "Is this a question about *who, what, where, when,* or *how*?" It asks about "a major industry." It is asking *what*, not *where*, which eliminates choice (B) right away. The correct answer is (A) "agriculture."

Look at the list of topics below. Would they probably be asking *who, what, where, when*, or *how*? (You may be right sometimes if you suggest more than one.)

- maps
- climate
- resources
- people
- history

Tips That Help

Social studies is all about people and places. It can be difficult at times to remember lots of names and events. But to perform your best on a social studies section, it helps to ask yourself a question about the question: *who, what, where, when,* or *how*.

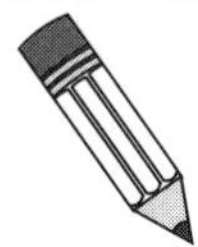

Now try the practice tests, listening to your teacher's directions.

Social Studies: World History Part I

Directions: Choose the correct answer to each question.

Prehistory

1. Prehistoric people are human beings who lived before __________ was invented about 5,500 years ago.
   (A) art (C) writing
   (B) metal (D) trade

2. The first human beings may have lived about __________ years ago.
   (F) one billion (H) 100 million
   (G) two million (J) 60 million

3. Which two kinds of evidence improves our understanding of prehistoric people?
   (A) temples and boats
   (B) tools and fossils
   (C) sacred writings and art
   (D) coins and caves

4. The theory that human beings changed their physical structure over times is called
   (F) erectus. (H) slow growth.
   (G) evolution. (J) hunter/gatherer.

5. Which is the only researcher who would probably NOT be involved in studying prehistoric people?
   (A) an archeologist
   (B) a meteorologist
   (C) a geologist
   (D) an anthropologist

6. So far, the best place in the world to find the earliest evidence of humans is
   (F) Europe. (H) Africa.
   (G) Asia. (J) Canada.

7. Most prehistoric tools that are found are made of
   (A) metal. (C) bone.
   (B) wood. (D) stone.

8. Scientists usually identify the first human species as
   (F) Lucy. (H) Piltdown Man.
   (G) Homo Erectus. (J) Leakey.

9. Which is NOT true of Neanderthals in Europe?
   (A) They used fire.
   (B) They lived in caves at times.
   (C) They buried their dead.
   (D) They did not hunt.

10. Cave art, beads, and tiny carvings are the products of
    (F) Homo erectus.
    (G) Cro-Magnons.
    (H) Neanderthals.
    (J) none of the above.

11. Most researchers believe prehistoric people reached the North American continent by
    (A) boat from Europe.
    (B) by a land bridge from northern Asia.
    (C) by migrating north from South America.
    (D) by unknown means.

12. Which is NOT considered an important step leading to the rise of civilization?
    (F) the invention of pottery
    (G) the invention of metalworking
    (H) the practice of hunting
    (J) the invention of writing

True or False

13. Homo sapien means "human being."
    (A) True (B) False

14. As the human species changed, the brain enlarged in size.
    (A) True (B) False

15. Prehistoric people are found only in Africa.
    (A) True (B) False

16. Prehistoric people didn't stay in one place until they began to farm.
    (A) True (B) False

GO →

The Fertile Crescent

17. One of the most fertile regions of the ancient world lay between the Tigris and Euphrates rivers in southern
    (A) China. (C) Africa.
    (B) Mesopotamia. (D) Israel.

18. By the 5000s B.C., many people had settled in villages in the lower part of the Tigris-Euphrates Valley, an area later called
    (F) the Nile.
    (G) the Mediterranean.
    (H) Sumer.
    (J) Asia.

19. By about 3500 B.C., these people had invented the first form of writing of wedge-shaped characters later called
    (A) cuneiform. (C) code.
    (B) hieroglyphics. (D) the Bible.

20. The towering temples of these ancient people in the Tigris-Euphrates valley were called
    (F) pyramids. (H) babels.
    (G) kingdoms. (J) ziggurats.

21. During the 2300s B.C., a Semitic king, ________ of Akkad, conquered Sumer. He united all Mesopotamia under his rule, creating the world's first empire.
    (A) David (C) Pharaoh
    (B) Sargon (D) Alexander

22. The largest and most powerful city in this area was
    (F) Cairo. (H) Babylon.
    (G) Rome. (J) Ishkabbible.

23. One of the kings of this city, ________, created one of the first law codes in history.
    (A) Cyrus the Great
    (B) Nebuchadnezzar II
    (C) Hammurabi
    (D) Alexander the Great

24. It was the invention of ________ that made possible the development of civilization.
    (F) iron (H) sculpture
    (G) farming (J) weapons

25. The hair of domestic animals and fibers from such plants as cotton and flax were used to make the first
    (A) blankets. (C) pottery.
    (B) textiles. (D) bricks.

26. People in this region and Ancient Egypt used a special class of professional writers to kept their records called
    (F) priests. (H) artisans.
    (G) scribes. (J) mathematicians.

27. Which is a piece of literature from the Fertile Crescent?
    (A) Camelot
    (B) the Epic of Gilgamesh
    (C) the trial of Socrates
    (D) the life of the Buddha

28. Babylonians also studied the night sky, believing that the stars and planets influenced the lives of people. This is called
    (F) astronomy. (H) portents.
    (G) star-gazing. (J) astrology.

GO →

Middle Ages

29. The Middle Ages is a period in European history from about
    - (A) 400 B.C. to 1700 A.D.
    - (B) 400 A.D. to 1500 A.D.
    - (C) 1500 A.D. to 1900 A.D.
    - (D) 1500 B.C. to 1500 A.D.

30. The Middle Ages developed slowly under the influence of such peoples as the
    - (F) Irish, Scots, and English.
    - (G) Saxons, Goths, Visigoths.
    - (H) Italians, Swiss, French.
    - (J) Davidians, Huns, Hindus.

31. As Roman law collapsed, superstitions about right and wrong replaced it, such as
    - (A) trial by combat.
    - (B) trial by ordeal.
    - (C) trial by jury.
    - (D) a & b

32. By the 800s, peasants in Europe often lived on _____________ ruled by wealthy landlords.
    - (F) estates
    - (G) manors
    - (H) villages
    - (J) castles

33. People left towns to live in the countryside, and the middle class disappeared, mainly because _________ had stopped without Roman encouragement.
    - (A) fighting
    - (B) trade
    - (C) fairness
    - (D) religion

34. The great civilizing influence of the Middle Ages that taught people to read and write was
    - (F) the lords of castles.
    - (G) the nobility.
    - (H) the Christian Church.
    - (J) the English.

35. Which was NOT an activity of the popes, bishops, and leaders of the church?
    - (A) collecting taxes
    - (B) maintaining courts of law
    - (C) building hospitals
    - (D) starting colonies

36. Which BEST describes feudalism in the Middle Ages?
    - (F) A king ruled a kingdom.
    - (G) Noblemen who controlled land, called fiefs, had all the military, political and economic power.
    - (H) Knights rode forth to protect kingdoms.
    - (J) Serfs worked the land without pay.

37. Pledging loyalty and professional service to a lord made a man the lord's
    - (A) thane.
    - (B) kinsman.
    - (C) knight.
    - (D) vassal.

38. England became the strongest feudal state in Europe under the invader, _________, or the Duke of Normandy as he was also titled.
    - (F) Ethelred the Unready
    - (G) Pepin the Short
    - (H) Charlemagne
    - (J) William the Conqueror

39. The Church did not practice feudalism, but its biggest threat for controlling powerful people was _____________ from the faith.
    - (A) taxation
    - (B) excommunication
    - (C) isolation
    - (D) suspension

40. Lords fought as knights for honor. The rules governing how a knight should live was called
    - (F) combat.
    - (G) tournament.
    - (H) chivalry.
    - (J) loyalty.

➢ STOP ➣

Social Studies: World History Part II

Directions: Choose the correct answer for each question.

Ancient Asia and Africa

1. ____________has been called the "birthplace of the human race."
   (A) Europe (C) The United States
   (B) Africa (D) Egypt

2. The rise of the religion, _______, became one of the most important developments in African history, leading to an empire in Northern Africa.
   (F) Christianity (H) Islam
   (G) Judaism (J) Shintoism

3. Camel ________ that crossed the Sahara spread trade, religion, and literature across Western Africa.
   (A) trains (C) trading posts
   (B) caravans (D) camps

True or False

4. A series of rulers from the same family, like those that ruled early China, is called a dynasty.
   (A) True (B) False

5. Japan has the world's oldest living civilization.
   (A) True (B) False

6. Civilization in India began in the Indus Valley between India and Pakistan.
   (A) True (B) False

7. The earliest known people to have united much of India were the Aryans.
   (A) True (B) False

Matching

8. Vasco da Gama (F) Mongul conqueror of Asian land
9. Genghis Khan (G) tried to extend his empire to India but was forced to turn back
10. Ashoka (H) first European explorer to reach India
11. Alexander the Great (J) Indian emperor who converted to Buddhism

12. caste system (A) currently the largest religion of India
13. the Upanishads (B) Hindu sacred writings
14. Siddhartha Gautama (C) all persons divided into social levels
15. Hinduism (D) founder of Buddhism

GO →

Ancient Greece

16. Greek civilization developed mainly in small
    - (F) towns.
    - (G) camps.
    - (H) city-states.
    - (J) countries.

17. Although they differed from place to place, the Greeks all called themselves
    - (A) Romans.
    - (B) Hellenes.
    - (C) Spartans.
    - (D) Alexandrines.

18. Greeks established the world's first
    - (F) monarchies.
    - (G) communistic states.
    - (H) colonies.
    - (J) democracies.

19. Greeks called people different from themselves
    - (A) barbarians.
    - (B) outlanders.
    - (C) serfs.
    - (D) alternators.

20. Greek civilization seems to have reached its peak during the
    - (F) the 5th century A.D.
    - (G) the 5th century B.C.
    - (H) the 20th century.
    - (J) the time after the Roman Empire.

21. In the Greek world, women, slaves, and serfs were all considered
    - (A) citizens.
    - (B) non-citizens.
    - (C) foreigners.
    - (D) none of these.

22. Who of the following was NOT a Greek philosopher?
    - (F) Socrates
    - (G) Archimedes
    - (H) Plato
    - (J) Aristotle

23. Which one is NOT associated with the Greeks?
    - (A) mathematics
    - (B) science
    - (C) exploration
    - (D) art

24. At first, government in Greece was run by a class of wealthy men. This kind of government is called a(n) __________.
    - (F) tyranny
    - (G) oligarchy
    - (H) monarchy
    - (J) republic

25. Sparta was not devoted to citizen involvement and government, the way Athens was. In Sparta, the most important thing was
    - (A) gaining wealth.
    - (B) trading with foreigners.
    - (C) creating art.
    - (D) training to become a soldier.

26. The first major civilization in the region of Greece arose on _______, an island.
    - (F) Sardis
    - (G) Elba
    - (H) Crete
    - (J) Cyprus

27. The mainland Greeks demonstrated their ability to control the region when they defeated the city of _________, an event described by the poet Homer.
    - (A) Sparta
    - (B) Troy
    - (C) Constantinople
    - (D) Thebes

28. Before the rise of democracy, some city-states were controlled by men who seized power. The Greeks called them
    - (F) tyrants.
    - (G) kings.
    - (H) plutarchs.
    - (J) olafs.

29. The Greeks not only fought among themselves, but as a culture they faced their greatest threat from
    - (A) Africa.
    - (B) Persia.
    - (C) Asia.
    - (D) Jerusalem.

➢ **STOP** ➣

Ancient Rome

1. The people of about 600 B.C. who turned Rome from a village of farmers into a city were the
   (A) Minoans. (C) Etruscans.
   (B) Gauls. (D) Senators.

2. Romans overthrew their king and created a
   (F) democracy. (H) monarchy.
   (G) republic. (J) tyranny.

3. Two classes of people struggled for power in Rome: the patricians, who were wealthy, and the __________, or ordinary citizens.
   (A) demos (C) serfs
   (B) plebians (D) shepherds

4. The most powerful government body of Rome was the
   (F) Senate. (H) consul.
   (G) judiciary. (J) Pantheon.

5. Which is TRUE about how the Roman empire treated conquered lands?
   (A) The Romans took away all the resources they could.
   (B) The Romans left the people's culture alone.
   (C) The Romans insisted conquered people be like them.
   (D) The Romans forced conquered people to evacuate.

6. Which did the Roman army NOT do in conquered lands?
   (F) build roads, bridges, and aqueducts
   (G) introduce Roman currency
   (H) introduce Roman law
   (J) enslave the population

7. Rome's most powerful opponent for control of the Mediterranean Sea was
   (A) Athens. (C) Carthage.
   (B) Madrid. (D) Troy.

8. Leaders such as Julius Caesar seized power and became emperors who ignored the Senate because
   (F) Rome became an empire.
   (G) Rome began to suffer from slave revolts, discontent, and corruption.
   (H) the empire was shrinking.
   (J) problems in Jerusalem were getting out of hand.

9. Powerful emperors ushered a long period of peace from approximately 50 B.C. to 150 A.D., which is known as the
   (A) Golden Age.
   (B) Dark Ages.
   (C) Roman Times.
   (D) Pax Romana.

10. Normally, the Roman Empire tolerated different religions, but one religion caused widespread disobedience. It was
    (F) Islam.
    (G) Judaism.
    (H) Christianity.
    (J) pagan worship.

GO →

Ancient Egypt

Directions: Read the passage below and choose the correct answer to the questions.

A pyramid is an apt figure for illustrating the political order of ancient Egypt. The pointed capstone at the top is the pharaoh. Then beneath him are gradually thickening layers of ministers of state, governors of districts, mayors, priests, and officials with all sorts of duties; then artisans and craftsmen; and on the bottom, a broad base of peasants and slaves.

The word "pharaoh" literally means "great house," but we use it as another name for "king." The pharaoh is respected and obeyed so that the gods will bless him and Egypt will prosper. Most pharaohs are from groups of rulers that are related by birth or marriage. A pharaoh may either be born to a ruling family or he can marry into a ruling family. Pharaohs by birth are usually the oldest son of the king; pharaohs by marriage are usually men who marry the ruling king's oldest daughter. This family of rulers is known as a dynasty.

Harmony in Egyptian society, and in the natural world, was thought to flow downward from the pharaoh, who was both high priest and ruler of Egypt, at the same time. In Egyptian artwork, the king's symbols for his dual role were the crook and the flail. In one hand, the king holds a shepherd's crook, identifying him as the caretaker of Egypt's people, a flock that needed his guidance. In the other, he grasps a whip, a flail, also seen in the hand of Osiris, the god of the dead. The whip is associated with magic and tradition.

Downward from the king, the line of authority extended through bureaucratic layers that ran the length of Egypt. The king appointed one vizier (*tjat*) for Upper Egypt and one for lower. A vizier named Rekmire was so proud of tasks laid upon him by the king that he had them written on the walls of his tomb. The pharaoh told him to be watchful over everything that was done and that the office of the vizier is the support of the whole land. A vizier was not to show respect of persons to princes or councilors and not to make slaves of people for himself.

A vizier was in communication with the pharaoh almost daily, either in person or by messenger. He reported on territorial disputes, kept an up-to-date cattle and herd census, supervised state projects including dike repair and temple building, and passed along gossip about princes and governors who needed watching. Each document—tax records, storehouse receipts, census records—had to have his personal seal to be considered authentic.

The pharaoh personally appointed all ministers and officials everywhere in Egypt. Often, titles were bestowed from the father to the son. Families held on to posts for generations. Like the pharaoh, the duties of officials were both civic and religious at the same time. Tax collectors, mayors, and temple scribes, for example, participated in religious ceremonies.

To those who served the interests of the people well, the pharaoh could bestow special favors and honors. A summons to approach the "Window of Appearance" was an intimate honor. Twice a year, a cushion was laid on a windowsill of one of the palaces. The king would appear, accompanied by family members and courtiers. The honoree would approach between two tall pylons and down an avenue of trees to receive his lord's personal thanks for exceptional service. The reward might be gold, or promotion to a higher office.

GO →

Ancient Egypt *(cont.)*

11. The political organization was like an upside down pyramid.
    (A) True (B) False

12. The flail, held by the pharaoh, is meant to stand for his harsh justice.
    (A) True (B) False

13. The vizier Rekmire was honored to be appointed by the pharaoh.
    (A) True (B) False

14. Which BEST describes the political organization of Ancient Egypt?
    (F) cruel and unjust
    (G) highly organized
    (H) corrupt and confusing
    (J) superstitious

15. The literal definition of *pharaoh* is
    (A) "great god."
    (B) "great house."
    (C) "president."
    (D) "governor."

16. Which of the following is NOT a task of the office of the vizier?
    (F) reporting on territorial disputes
    (G) supervising state projects
    (H) passing gossip about princes and governors
    (J) fighting in the military

17. Which BEST describes the purpose of the "Window of Appearance"?
    (A) a court
    (B) a window to stand at for parades
    (C) an opportunity to meet the pharaoh in person
    (D) a museum honoring the pharaoh

18. Which would be the BEST title for this passage?
    (F) The Land of Egypt
    (G) Egypt and its People
    (H) Leaders of Long Ago
    (J) Power Flowed Downward from the Pharaoh

➢ STOP ≺

Directions: Identify the word that is being described.

1. An expanse of water that contains many scattered islands.

   (A) harbor (B) river (C) archipelago (D) ocean

2. A human-made waterway that is used for boats and irrigation.

   (F) canal (G) river (H) mouth (J) harbor

3. A high, steep slope of rock.

   (A) canyon (B) cliff (C) desert (D) fjord

4. A very dry region that is often sandy and without plants.

   (F) valley (G) volcano (H) desert (J) plain

5. The place where a river flows into a larger body of water.

   (A) fjord (B) mouth (C) gulf (D) harbor

6. A lowland area between hills or mountains.

   (F) plain (G) plateau (H) swamp (J) valley

7. A wooded area that has an annual rainfall of at least 100 inches.

   (A) desert (B) rain forest (C) island (D) bay

8. A sheltered area of water where ships can anchor safely.

   (F) dam (G) fjord (H) harbor (J) strait

9. A piece of land that extends into a body of water.

   (A) cliff (B) glacier (C) cape (D) mouth

10. A large body of ice that moves slowly down a mountain.

    (F) fjord (G) glacier (H) tributary (J) gulf

11. A narrow waterway that connects two larger bodies of water.

    (A) strait (B) isthmus (C) lake (D) rapids

12. A narrow strip of land that has water on either side and connects two larger bodies of land.

    (F) peninsula (G) isthmus (H) canal (J) mountain range

➢ STOP ➣

Directions: Choose the correct answer to fill each blank.

(A) compromise	(C) Gilded Age	(F) Reconstruction	(H) states' rights
(B) Louisiana	(D) Civil War	(G) slavery	(J) frontier

After the purchase of ______________, Americans began to think of moving further westward to get
1

land for themselves. As their settlements expanded, however, the issue of ___________ became part
2

of the national debate every time a state applied for admission to the Union. Eventually, all attempts at

______________ had failed. Southern states seceded from the Union, claiming that ______________
3 4

were not being respected. It fell to newly-elected President Lincoln to fight "the rebellion" as he called

it, or as it is better known, the ________________. After five years of fighting and Lincoln's
5

assassination, a period of harsh laws and rebuilding was forced on the South. The North called it

______________; the South called it punishment. A different United States emerged, one where
6

fortunes were suddenly made and lost, and greed corrupted many public figures. Mark Twain

nicknamed this period the ___________, meaning it looked flashy but was deceiving. Meanwhile,
7

the last of the American ____________ was settled.
8

GO →

Directions: Choose the correct answer to fill each blank.

(A) nation	(D) people	(H) American Revolution
(B) Asia	(F) New World	(J) common man
(C) French and Indian War	(G) debt	

Explorers were looking for a short route to ___________(9), but they landed in America instead. Many European nations began to explore this ___________(10) to see whether there was any profit to be made. By 1763 England had established itself as master over North America. England provided protection to colonists during the ___________(11), but later the colonists did not want to pay for the help. This issue and taxation led to worsening relations, which eventually caused the ___________(12). The new United States had to decide whether it would act as a ___________(13) or remain thirteen separate governments. In addition, a related issue about who was responsible for the national ___________(14) raised serious questions. When Thomas Jefferson took office as President in 1801, he promised not to favor any political party. He favored "government by the ___________(15)," which would become the theme of the federal government for many years. Andrew Jackson strongly played on this theme as President, preferring the ___________(16) as his model of an American.

GO →

Constitution

Directions: Match the term with the correct definition.

17. Articles of Confederation
18. act
19. bicameral
20. bill
21. Bill of Rights
22. census
23. Civil Rights
24. compromise

(A) rights that belong to all persons who are citizens of a state or the United States
(B) composed of two legislative bodies, or houses, through which all bills must pass
(C) the first ten amendments to the United States Constitution
(D) the name of the first United States Constitution used during the American Revolution
(F) to come to agreement by concession
(G) a bill which has passed both houses of Congress and has been signed by the President or passed over his veto, thus becoming law
(H) a proposed law, printed, and presented to Congress for action that may lead to its adoption through the legislative process
(J) population count held every 10 years, as described in the U.S. Constitution

---

25. desegregation
26. implied powers
27. executive branch
28. filibuster
29. gerrymandering
30. impeachment
31. enumerated powers
32. joint resolution

(A) the President and departments that carry out the laws of the federal government
(B) the process of ending separation of the races, especially in public places
(C) specific powers of Congress, listed in Article I, Section 8 of the Constitution
(D) drawing of a strangely-shaped congressional district to give an advantage to a particular party
(F) indicting and trying a federal official for a crime
(G) powers necessary for Congress to carry out its expressed or enumerated powers
(H) a resolution introduced at the same time and in the same form in both the House and the Senate
(J) a delaying tactic used in the Senate to prevent a vote on a bill or resolution

---

33. judicial branch
34. legislative branch
35. naturalization
36. pocket veto
37. quorum
38. separation of powers
39. The State of the Union
40. veto

(A) the process of granting full citizenship to those of foreign birth
(B) the President's assessment of the condition of the United States, delivered to Congress, as required by the Constitution
(C) the minimum number of House and Senate members necessary to conduct business on the floor of each chamber
(D) the courts, which interpret the laws
(F) the decision of the President not to take action on the signing of a bill near the end of a session of Congress
(G) division of the powers of government among three branches—legislative, executive, and judicial
(H) disapproval by the President of a bill or joint resolution
(J) Congress, which is the division of government that makes laws

➢ STOP ≺

Fine Arts: Music, Dance, and Theater

Directions: Choose the correct answer for each question.

Music

1. Which has the highest pitch of woodwinds?
   (A) saxophone
   (B) clarinet
   (C) piccolo
   (D) flute

2. Which has the lowest pitch?
   (F) trumpet
   (G) tuba
   (H) trombone
   (J) French horn

3. Which one is NOT a percussion instrument?
   (A) kettledrum
   (B) cymbal
   (C) tambourine
   (D) organ

4. Which is NOT an element of music?
   (F) melody
   (G) harmony
   (H) effect
   (J) rhythm

5. Which is NOT a type of musical note?
   (A) sharp
   (B) beat
   (C) flat
   (D) whole

6. The sounding together of three or more notes is called
   (F) melody.
   (G) fineness.
   (H) barbershop singing.
   (J) harmony.

7. Periods of silence in music are called
   (A) pauses. (C) bars.
   (B) rests. (D) measures.

8. The way beats are grouped in measures is called the
   (F) meter. (H) beat.
   (G) rhythm. (J) time.

9. Symphony music composed for operas and ballets is called
   (A) rock. (C) folk.
   (B) jazz. (D) classical.

10. __________ first became popular about 1900 among blacks of the Southern United States. It combines the complex rhythms of African music and the harmony of Western music.
    (F) Country
    (G) Folk
    (H) Rock
    (J) Jazz

11. ____________ music comes from the folk music of Caucasians living in farming areas of the Southern United States and other American traditional music.
    (A) Jazz
    (B) Country
    (C) Ballet
    (D) Gospel

12. __________________, such as "West Side Story," is a type of play that tells a story through a combination of spoken dialogue, songs, and dances.
    (F) A symphony
    (G) A ballet
    (H) A musical
    (J) A concert

GO →

Dance

13. Most kinds of social dancing includes _______ and rhythms.
   (A) clapping
   (B) steps
   (C) audiences
   (D) orchestras

14. __________ is the pattern of timing around which the dance movement is organized.
   (F) Script
   (G) Rhythm
   (H) Meter
   (J) Tap

15. Which kind of dancing requires upright posture, arms outward, and raising up on the toe?
   (A) folk (C) ballet
   (B) jazz (D) tap

16. What kind of dancing includes polkas, square dancing, and Irish jigs?
   (F) modern (H) ballet
   (G) folk (J) jazz

17. American ____________, such as "West Side Story" and "Singin' in the Rain," include highly imaginative, original dance numbers.
   (A) ballets (C) operas
   (B) musicals (D) skits

18. Currently, a type of dancing from the 1940s that's popular, and done to the music of a big band is
   (F) tango.
   (G) Charleston.
   (H) jitterbug.
   (J) swing.

19. Which of the following is NOT a fine art?
   (A) ballet
   (B) literature
   (C) computer programming
   (D) sculpture

20. Which of the following is NOT a performing art?
   (F) music (H) dance
   (G) horseback riding (J) theater

Theater

21. Which is the BEST definition of theater?
   (A) a film by or about Shakespeare
   (B) an art form in which a script is acted out by performers
   (C) a creative kind of pretending
   (D) costumes, lights, stage

22. Which is NOT part of the theater experience?
   (F) script (H) audience
   (G) stage (J) camera

23. Which of the following jobs would NOT be found in a theater?
   (A) director
   (B) driver
   (C) lighting designer
   (D) performer

24. What does the director of a play do?
   (F) advertises the play
   (G) writes a review of the play
   (H) writes the play
   (J) guides the performers in interpreting their roles

25. What is the auditorium?
   (A) It's where the audience sits.
   (B) It's where the actors perform.
   (C) It's where the tickets are taken.
   (D) It's where the costumes are kept.

26. Which is NOT a type of stage?
   (F) the proscenium stage
   (G) platform stage
   (H) the grandstand stage
   (J) the theater-in-the-round stage

➢ STOP ➣

Computers and Technology: Background

Directions: Choose the word that completes the sentence the best.

Computers process ________ (1) such as numbers, words, still pictures, moving pictures, and sounds. Millions of people and organizations communicate with one another over a network of computers called the ________ (2). Almost all computers are electronic digital computers. They are called digital because they process information as units of electric charge representing ________ (3).

Digital computers are one of two general kinds of computers. The other kind are calculating devices called ________ (4) computers. Computer information is measured in multiples of ________ (5).

A computer is made up of many parts. The ________ (6), also known as the central processing unit (CPU), does the actual computing. Memory ________ (7) hold data and processing instructions for use by the microprocessor. The computer receives data through input devices, such as a ________ (8). Storage devices, which include ________ (9) and tapes, hold data and instructions for transfer to memory. Output devices, such as a ________ (10), show results of the computer work.

The number of computers in use has risen from about 100,000 worldwide in the early 1960s to hundreds of millions today. The technology of ________ (11), or programs, is also advancing rapidly.

Personal computers are usually used by one person at a time. A ________ (12) consists of a group of computers connected by telephone lines or other communications cables. The central computer is called the ________ (13). Personal computers used in schools and businesses are usually referred to as ________ (14). In a typical network, individuals operating the personal computers obtain copies of information from the server.

Home users of computers do some of the same kinds of work on personal data. They use ________ (15) programs for private correspondence, financial software, and database management programs for address lists and recipes. Individuals also use their home computers to play games and surf the Internet.

________ (16) are the fastest computers, and they use the largest storage systems. They can solve more complex problems and handle more information than any other category of computer. They are also the largest computers.

GO →

1. (A) scenes
   (B) information
   (C) electricity
   (D) pulses

2. (F) telecommuting
   (G) airwaves
   (H) Internet
   (J) supercomputer

3. (A) data
   (B) numbers
   (C) electrons
   (D) taps

4. (F) analog
   (G) timeshare
   (H) mainframe
   (J) clock

5. (A) megs
   (B) pins
   (C) bytes
   (D) words

6. (F) motherboard
   (G) cards
   (H) units
   (J) microprocessor

7. (A) cells
   (B) chips
   (C) wiring
   (D) screens

8. (F) typing
   (G) pad
   (H) keyboard
   (J) cursor

9. (A) cables
   (B) disks
   (C) printers
   (D) warehouses

10. (F) mouse
    (G) printer
    (H) robot
    (J) webmaster

11. (A) software
    (B) modems
    (C) search engines
    (D) laptops

12. (F) web
    (G) network
    (H) cell
    (J) agency

13. (A) hub
    (B) link
    (C) server
    (D) span

14. (F) cubicles
    (G) desks
    (H) learning booths
    (J) workstations

15. (A) data
    (B) word-processing
    (C) calculators
    (D) free

16. (F) IBMs
    (G) Clones
    (H) Crunchers
    (J) Mainframes

➤ STOP ➤

Computers and Technology: Vocabulary

Directions: Read the definition and choose the correct term being described.

1. In the United States, common ones are edu (education), gov (government agency), net (network related), com (commercial), org (non-profit and research organizations).

   (A) locations (B) domains (C) sites (D) notes

2. Save to diskette.

   (F) download (G) paste (H) copy (J) highlight

3. Searches for word(s) keyed in document in screen only; useful to locate a term in a long document:

   (A) edit (B) scroll (C) find (D) address

4. A format for Web documents that divides the screen into segments, each with a scroll bar as if it were as "window" within the window.

   (F) frames (G) window (H) page (J) view

5. Way to combine terms using "AND," "OR," "AND NOT" and sometimes "NEAR." Parentheses may be used to sequence operations and group words.

   (A) word clusters (B) groups (C) combos (D) boolean logic

6. Way to store in your computer sites to which you wish to return.

   (F) placeholder (G) bookmark (H) save (J) scroll

7. Software programs that enable you to view WWW documents.

   (A) keywords (B) searchers (C) browsers (D) mosaics

8. The address in another document, so that if you click on the highlighted text or button, you automatically go to another site.

   (F) link (G) click (H) paste (J) underline

9. It automatically submits your keyword search to several other search tools and retrieves results from all their databases.

   (A) data processor (B) retrieval.com (C) searcher (D) meta-search engine

10. Moving up or down within a document in your screen:

    (F) direction (G) pointing (H) scrolling (J) browsing

11. Where you temporarily store Web pages you have visited in your computer; a copy of documents you retrieve is also stored here.

    (A) drive (B) cache (C) database (D) megs

12. Computer that provides Web documents to clients or users.

    (F) host (G) patchmaker (H) online (J) terminal

13. The vast collection of interconnected networks:

    (A) family (B) gopher (C) http (D) Internet

14. A word searched for in a search command.

    (F) find (G) return (H) keyword (J) locate

➢ STOP ≺

Language Arts: Reading Competencies
Page: 15

Test

1. Ⓐ Ⓑ Ⓒ Ⓓ
2. Ⓕ Ⓖ Ⓗ Ⓙ
3. Ⓐ Ⓑ Ⓒ Ⓓ
4. Ⓕ Ⓖ Ⓗ Ⓙ
5. Ⓐ Ⓑ Ⓒ Ⓓ
6. Ⓕ Ⓖ Ⓗ Ⓙ

Language Arts: Reading Competencies
Pages: 16–17

Test

1. Ⓐ Ⓑ Ⓒ Ⓓ
2. Ⓕ Ⓖ Ⓗ Ⓙ
3. Ⓐ Ⓑ Ⓒ Ⓓ
4. Ⓕ Ⓖ Ⓗ Ⓙ

Language Arts : Reading Competencies
Pages: 18–19

Test

1. Ⓐ Ⓑ Ⓒ Ⓓ
2. Ⓕ Ⓖ Ⓗ Ⓙ
3. Ⓐ Ⓑ Ⓒ Ⓓ
4. Ⓕ Ⓖ Ⓗ Ⓙ
5. Ⓐ Ⓑ Ⓒ Ⓓ
6. Ⓕ Ⓖ Ⓗ Ⓙ

Language Arts: Reading Competencies
Page: 20

Test

1. Ⓐ Ⓑ Ⓒ Ⓓ
2. Ⓕ Ⓖ Ⓗ Ⓙ
3. Ⓐ Ⓑ Ⓒ Ⓓ
4. Ⓕ Ⓖ Ⓗ Ⓙ
5. Ⓐ Ⓑ Ⓒ Ⓓ

Student Answer Sheets *(cont.)*

Language Arts: Reading Competencies
Pages: 21–22

Test

1. Ⓐ Ⓑ Ⓒ Ⓓ
2. Ⓕ Ⓖ Ⓗ Ⓙ
3. Ⓐ Ⓑ Ⓒ Ⓓ
4. Ⓕ Ⓖ Ⓗ Ⓙ

Language Arts: Writing Competencies
Pages: 23–27

Test

1. Ⓐ Ⓑ Ⓒ
2. Ⓕ Ⓖ Ⓗ
3. Ⓐ Ⓑ Ⓒ
4. Ⓕ Ⓖ Ⓗ
5. Ⓐ Ⓑ Ⓒ
6. Ⓕ Ⓖ Ⓗ
7. Ⓐ Ⓑ Ⓒ
8. Ⓕ Ⓖ Ⓗ
9. Ⓐ Ⓑ Ⓒ
10. Ⓕ Ⓖ Ⓗ
11. Ⓐ Ⓑ Ⓒ
12. Ⓕ Ⓖ Ⓗ
13. Ⓐ Ⓑ Ⓒ
14. Ⓕ Ⓖ Ⓗ
15. Ⓐ Ⓑ Ⓒ
16. Ⓕ Ⓖ Ⓗ
17. Ⓐ Ⓑ Ⓒ
18. Ⓕ Ⓖ Ⓗ
19. Ⓐ Ⓑ Ⓒ
20. Ⓕ Ⓖ Ⓗ
21. Ⓐ Ⓑ Ⓒ
22. Ⓕ Ⓖ Ⓗ
23. Ⓐ Ⓑ Ⓒ
24. Ⓕ Ⓖ Ⓗ
25. Ⓐ Ⓑ Ⓒ
26. Ⓕ Ⓖ Ⓗ
27. Ⓐ Ⓑ Ⓒ
28. Ⓕ Ⓖ Ⓗ
29. Ⓐ Ⓑ Ⓒ
30. Ⓕ Ⓖ Ⓗ
31. Ⓐ Ⓑ Ⓒ
32. Ⓕ Ⓖ Ⓗ
33. Ⓐ Ⓑ Ⓒ
34. Ⓕ Ⓖ Ⓗ
35. Ⓐ Ⓑ Ⓒ
36. Ⓕ Ⓖ Ⓗ
37. Ⓐ Ⓑ Ⓒ

Student Answer Sheets *(cont.)*

Language Arts: Writing Competencies
Pages: 28–29

Test

Language Arts: Library Research
Pages: 30–32

Test

1. Ⓐ Ⓑ Ⓒ Ⓓ
2. Ⓕ Ⓖ Ⓗ Ⓙ
3. Ⓐ Ⓑ Ⓒ Ⓓ
4. Ⓕ Ⓖ Ⓗ Ⓙ
5. Ⓐ Ⓑ Ⓒ Ⓓ
6. Ⓕ Ⓖ Ⓗ Ⓙ
7. Ⓐ Ⓑ Ⓒ Ⓓ
8. Ⓕ Ⓖ Ⓗ Ⓙ
9. Ⓐ Ⓑ Ⓒ Ⓓ
10. Ⓕ Ⓖ Ⓗ Ⓙ
11. Ⓐ Ⓑ Ⓒ Ⓓ
12. Ⓕ Ⓖ Ⓗ Ⓙ
13. Ⓐ Ⓑ Ⓒ Ⓓ
14. Ⓕ Ⓖ Ⓗ Ⓙ
15. Ⓐ Ⓑ Ⓒ Ⓓ
16. Ⓕ Ⓖ Ⓗ
17. Ⓐ Ⓑ Ⓒ
18. Ⓕ Ⓖ Ⓗ
19. Ⓐ Ⓑ Ⓒ
20. Ⓕ Ⓖ Ⓗ
21. Ⓐ Ⓑ Ⓒ Ⓓ
22. Ⓕ Ⓖ Ⓗ Ⓙ
23. Ⓐ Ⓑ Ⓒ Ⓓ
24. Ⓕ Ⓖ Ⓗ Ⓙ
25. Ⓐ Ⓑ Ⓒ Ⓓ
26. Ⓕ Ⓖ Ⓗ Ⓙ

Mathematics: Rational and Irrational Numbers
Page: 35

Test

1. Ⓐ Ⓑ
2. Ⓐ Ⓑ
3. Ⓐ Ⓑ
4. Ⓐ Ⓑ
5. Ⓐ Ⓑ
6. Ⓐ Ⓑ
7. Ⓐ Ⓑ Ⓒ Ⓓ
8. Ⓕ Ⓖ Ⓗ Ⓙ
9. Ⓐ Ⓑ Ⓒ Ⓓ
10. Ⓕ Ⓖ Ⓗ Ⓙ
11. Ⓐ Ⓑ Ⓒ Ⓓ
12. Ⓕ Ⓖ Ⓗ Ⓙ

Mathematics: Real Numbers Part I
Pages: 36–37

Test

1. Ⓐ Ⓑ Ⓒ Ⓓ
2. Ⓕ Ⓖ Ⓗ Ⓙ
3. Ⓐ Ⓑ Ⓒ Ⓓ
4. Ⓕ Ⓖ Ⓗ Ⓙ
5. Ⓐ Ⓑ Ⓒ Ⓓ
6. Ⓕ Ⓖ Ⓗ Ⓙ
7. Ⓐ Ⓑ Ⓒ Ⓓ
8. Ⓕ Ⓖ Ⓗ Ⓙ
9. Ⓐ Ⓑ Ⓒ Ⓓ
10. Ⓕ Ⓖ Ⓗ Ⓙ
11. Ⓐ Ⓑ Ⓒ Ⓓ
12. Ⓕ Ⓖ Ⓗ Ⓙ
13. Ⓐ Ⓑ Ⓒ Ⓓ
14. Ⓕ Ⓖ Ⓗ Ⓙ
15. Ⓐ Ⓑ Ⓒ Ⓓ
16. Ⓕ Ⓖ Ⓗ Ⓙ
17. Ⓐ Ⓑ Ⓒ Ⓓ
18. Ⓕ Ⓖ Ⓗ Ⓙ
19. Ⓐ Ⓑ Ⓒ Ⓓ
20. Ⓕ Ⓖ Ⓗ Ⓙ
21. Ⓐ Ⓑ Ⓒ Ⓓ
22. Ⓕ Ⓖ Ⓗ Ⓙ
23. Ⓐ Ⓑ Ⓒ Ⓓ

Mathematics: Real Numbers
Part II
Pages: 38–40

Test

1. Ⓐ Ⓑ Ⓒ Ⓓ
2. Ⓕ Ⓖ Ⓗ Ⓙ
3. Ⓐ Ⓑ Ⓒ Ⓓ
4. Ⓕ Ⓖ Ⓗ Ⓙ
5. Ⓐ Ⓑ Ⓒ Ⓓ
6. Ⓕ Ⓖ Ⓗ Ⓙ
7. Ⓐ Ⓑ Ⓒ Ⓓ
8. Ⓕ Ⓖ Ⓗ Ⓙ
9. Ⓐ Ⓑ Ⓒ Ⓓ
10. Ⓕ Ⓖ Ⓗ Ⓙ
11. Ⓐ Ⓑ Ⓒ Ⓓ
12. Ⓕ Ⓖ Ⓗ Ⓙ
13. Ⓐ Ⓑ Ⓒ Ⓓ
14. Ⓕ Ⓖ Ⓗ Ⓙ
15. Ⓐ Ⓑ Ⓒ Ⓓ
16. Ⓕ Ⓖ Ⓗ Ⓙ
17. Ⓐ Ⓑ Ⓒ Ⓓ
18. Ⓕ Ⓖ Ⓗ Ⓙ
19. Ⓐ Ⓑ Ⓒ Ⓓ
20. Ⓕ Ⓖ Ⓗ Ⓙ
21. Ⓐ Ⓑ Ⓒ Ⓓ
22. Ⓕ Ⓖ Ⓗ Ⓙ
23. Ⓐ Ⓑ Ⓒ Ⓓ
24. Ⓕ Ⓖ Ⓗ Ⓙ
25. Ⓐ Ⓑ Ⓒ Ⓓ
26. Ⓕ Ⓖ Ⓗ Ⓙ
27. Ⓐ Ⓑ Ⓒ Ⓓ
28. Ⓕ Ⓖ Ⓗ Ⓙ
29. Ⓐ Ⓑ Ⓒ Ⓓ
30. Ⓐ Ⓑ
31. Ⓐ Ⓑ
32. Ⓐ Ⓑ
33. Ⓐ Ⓑ
34. Ⓐ Ⓑ
35. Ⓐ Ⓑ
36. Ⓕ Ⓖ Ⓗ Ⓙ
37. Ⓐ Ⓑ Ⓒ Ⓓ
38. Ⓕ Ⓖ Ⓗ Ⓙ
39. Ⓐ Ⓑ Ⓒ Ⓓ
40. Ⓕ Ⓖ Ⓗ Ⓙ

Mathematics: Geometry
Page: 41

Test

1. Ⓐ Ⓑ Ⓒ Ⓓ
2. Ⓕ Ⓖ Ⓗ Ⓙ
3. Ⓐ Ⓑ Ⓒ Ⓓ
4. Ⓕ Ⓖ Ⓗ Ⓙ
5. Ⓐ Ⓑ Ⓒ Ⓓ
6. Ⓕ Ⓖ Ⓗ Ⓙ
7. Ⓐ Ⓑ Ⓒ Ⓓ
8. Ⓕ Ⓖ Ⓗ Ⓙ
9. Ⓐ Ⓑ Ⓒ Ⓓ
10. Ⓕ Ⓖ Ⓗ Ⓙ
11. Ⓐ Ⓑ Ⓒ Ⓓ
12. Ⓕ Ⓖ Ⓗ Ⓙ
13. Ⓐ Ⓑ Ⓒ Ⓓ
14. Ⓕ Ⓖ Ⓗ Ⓙ

Mathematics: Pre-Algebra
Page: 42

Test

1. Ⓐ Ⓑ Ⓒ Ⓓ
2. Ⓕ Ⓖ Ⓗ Ⓙ
3. Ⓐ Ⓑ Ⓒ Ⓓ
4. Ⓕ Ⓖ Ⓗ Ⓙ
5. Ⓐ Ⓑ Ⓒ Ⓓ
6. Ⓕ Ⓖ Ⓗ Ⓙ
7. Ⓐ Ⓑ Ⓒ Ⓓ
8. Ⓕ Ⓖ Ⓗ Ⓙ
9. Ⓐ Ⓑ Ⓒ Ⓓ
10. Ⓕ Ⓖ Ⓗ Ⓙ

Student Answer Sheets *(cont.)*

Science: Biology
Pages: 45–48

Test

1. Ⓐ Ⓑ Ⓒ Ⓓ
2. Ⓕ Ⓖ Ⓗ Ⓙ
3. Ⓐ Ⓑ Ⓒ Ⓓ
4. Ⓕ Ⓖ Ⓗ Ⓙ
5. Ⓐ Ⓑ Ⓒ Ⓓ
6. Ⓕ Ⓖ Ⓗ Ⓙ
7. Ⓐ Ⓑ Ⓒ Ⓓ
8. Ⓕ Ⓖ Ⓗ Ⓙ
9. Ⓐ Ⓑ
10. Ⓐ Ⓑ
11. Ⓐ Ⓑ
12. Ⓐ Ⓑ
13. Ⓐ Ⓑ
14. Ⓐ Ⓑ
15. Ⓐ Ⓑ Ⓒ Ⓓ
16. Ⓕ Ⓖ Ⓗ Ⓙ
17. Ⓐ Ⓑ Ⓒ Ⓓ
18. Ⓕ Ⓖ Ⓗ Ⓙ
19. Ⓐ Ⓑ Ⓒ Ⓓ
20. Ⓕ Ⓖ Ⓗ Ⓙ
21. Ⓐ Ⓑ
22. Ⓐ Ⓑ
23. Ⓐ Ⓑ
24. Ⓐ Ⓑ
25. Ⓐ Ⓑ
26. Ⓐ Ⓑ
27. Ⓐ Ⓑ
28. Ⓐ Ⓑ
29. Ⓐ Ⓑ
30. Ⓕ Ⓖ Ⓗ Ⓙ
31. Ⓐ Ⓑ Ⓒ Ⓓ
32. Ⓕ Ⓖ Ⓗ Ⓙ
33. Ⓐ Ⓑ Ⓒ Ⓓ
34. Ⓕ Ⓖ Ⓗ Ⓙ
35. Ⓐ Ⓑ
36. Ⓐ Ⓑ
37. Ⓐ Ⓑ
38. Ⓐ Ⓑ
39. Ⓐ Ⓑ Ⓒ Ⓓ
40. Ⓐ Ⓑ Ⓒ Ⓓ
41. Ⓐ Ⓑ Ⓒ Ⓓ
42. Ⓐ Ⓑ Ⓒ Ⓓ
43. Ⓕ Ⓖ Ⓗ Ⓙ
44. Ⓕ Ⓖ Ⓗ Ⓙ
45. Ⓕ Ⓖ Ⓗ Ⓙ
46. Ⓕ Ⓖ Ⓗ Ⓙ
47. Ⓐ Ⓑ Ⓒ Ⓓ
48. Ⓐ Ⓑ Ⓒ Ⓓ
49. Ⓐ Ⓑ Ⓒ Ⓓ
50. Ⓐ Ⓑ Ⓒ Ⓓ
51. Ⓕ Ⓖ Ⓗ Ⓙ
52. Ⓕ Ⓖ Ⓗ Ⓙ
53. Ⓕ Ⓖ Ⓗ Ⓙ
54. Ⓕ Ⓖ Ⓗ Ⓙ
55. Ⓐ Ⓑ Ⓒ Ⓓ
56. Ⓐ Ⓑ Ⓒ Ⓓ
57. Ⓐ Ⓑ Ⓒ Ⓓ
58. Ⓐ Ⓑ Ⓒ Ⓓ

Science: Chemistry
Pages: 49–50

Test

1. Ⓐ Ⓑ Ⓒ Ⓓ
2. Ⓕ Ⓖ Ⓗ Ⓙ
3. Ⓐ Ⓑ Ⓒ Ⓓ
4. Ⓕ Ⓖ Ⓗ Ⓙ
5. Ⓐ Ⓑ Ⓒ Ⓓ
6. Ⓕ Ⓖ Ⓗ Ⓙ
7. Ⓐ Ⓑ Ⓒ Ⓓ
8. Ⓕ Ⓖ Ⓗ Ⓙ
9. Ⓐ Ⓑ Ⓒ Ⓓ
10. Ⓕ Ⓖ Ⓗ Ⓙ
11. Ⓐ Ⓑ Ⓒ Ⓓ
12. Ⓕ Ⓖ Ⓗ Ⓙ
13. Ⓐ Ⓑ Ⓒ Ⓓ
14. Ⓕ Ⓖ Ⓗ Ⓙ
15. Ⓐ Ⓑ
16. Ⓐ Ⓑ
17. Ⓐ Ⓑ
18. Ⓐ Ⓑ
19. Ⓐ Ⓑ
20. Ⓐ Ⓑ
21. Ⓐ Ⓑ
22. Ⓐ Ⓑ
23. Ⓐ Ⓑ Ⓒ
24. Ⓐ Ⓑ Ⓒ
25. Ⓐ Ⓑ Ⓒ
26. Ⓐ Ⓑ Ⓒ
27. Ⓐ Ⓑ Ⓒ
28. Ⓐ Ⓑ Ⓒ
29. Ⓐ Ⓑ Ⓒ
30. Ⓐ Ⓑ Ⓒ

Science: Physics
Pages: 51–53

Test

1. Ⓐ Ⓑ Ⓒ Ⓓ
2. Ⓕ Ⓖ Ⓗ Ⓙ
3. Ⓐ Ⓑ Ⓒ Ⓓ
4. Ⓕ Ⓖ Ⓗ Ⓙ
5. Ⓐ Ⓑ
6. Ⓐ Ⓑ
7. Ⓐ Ⓑ
8. Ⓐ Ⓑ
9. Ⓐ Ⓑ
10. Ⓕ Ⓖ Ⓗ Ⓙ
11. Ⓐ Ⓑ Ⓒ Ⓓ
12. Ⓕ Ⓖ Ⓗ Ⓙ
13. Ⓐ Ⓑ Ⓒ Ⓓ
14. Ⓕ Ⓖ Ⓗ Ⓙ
15. Ⓐ Ⓑ Ⓒ Ⓓ
16. Ⓕ Ⓖ Ⓗ Ⓙ
17. Ⓐ Ⓑ Ⓒ Ⓓ
18. Ⓕ Ⓖ Ⓗ Ⓙ
19. Ⓐ Ⓑ Ⓒ Ⓓ
20. Ⓕ Ⓖ Ⓗ Ⓙ
21. Ⓐ Ⓑ
22. Ⓐ Ⓑ
23. Ⓐ Ⓑ
24. Ⓐ Ⓑ
25. Ⓐ Ⓑ
26. Ⓐ Ⓑ
27. Ⓐ Ⓑ
28. Ⓕ Ⓖ Ⓗ Ⓙ
29. Ⓐ Ⓑ Ⓒ Ⓓ
30. Ⓕ Ⓖ Ⓗ Ⓙ
31. Ⓐ Ⓑ Ⓒ Ⓓ
32. Ⓕ Ⓖ Ⓗ Ⓙ
33. Ⓐ Ⓑ Ⓒ Ⓓ
34. Ⓕ Ⓖ Ⓗ Ⓙ
35. Ⓐ Ⓑ Ⓒ Ⓓ
36. Ⓕ Ⓖ Ⓗ Ⓙ
37. Ⓐ Ⓑ Ⓒ Ⓓ
38. Ⓕ Ⓖ Ⓗ Ⓙ
39. Ⓐ Ⓑ Ⓒ Ⓓ
40. Ⓕ Ⓖ Ⓗ Ⓙ

Science: Geology
Pages: 54–55

Test

1. Ⓐ Ⓑ Ⓒ Ⓓ
2. Ⓕ Ⓖ Ⓗ Ⓙ
3. Ⓐ Ⓑ Ⓒ Ⓓ
4. Ⓕ Ⓖ Ⓗ Ⓙ
5. Ⓐ Ⓑ Ⓒ Ⓓ
6. Ⓕ Ⓖ Ⓗ Ⓙ
7. Ⓐ Ⓑ Ⓒ Ⓓ
8. Ⓕ Ⓖ Ⓗ Ⓙ
9. Ⓐ Ⓑ Ⓒ Ⓓ
10. Ⓕ Ⓖ Ⓗ Ⓙ
11. Ⓐ Ⓑ Ⓒ Ⓓ
12. Ⓕ Ⓖ Ⓗ Ⓙ
13. Ⓐ Ⓑ Ⓒ Ⓓ
14. Ⓕ Ⓖ Ⓗ Ⓙ
15. Ⓐ Ⓑ Ⓒ Ⓓ
16. Ⓕ Ⓖ Ⓗ Ⓙ
17. Ⓐ Ⓑ
18. Ⓐ Ⓑ
19. Ⓐ Ⓑ
20. Ⓐ Ⓑ
21. Ⓐ Ⓑ
22. Ⓐ Ⓑ
23. Ⓐ Ⓑ

Social Studies: World History
Part I
Pages: 58–60

Test

1. Ⓐ Ⓑ Ⓒ Ⓓ
2. Ⓕ Ⓖ Ⓗ Ⓙ
3. Ⓐ Ⓑ Ⓒ Ⓓ
4. Ⓕ Ⓖ Ⓗ Ⓙ
5. Ⓐ Ⓑ Ⓒ Ⓓ
6. Ⓕ Ⓖ Ⓗ Ⓙ
7. Ⓐ Ⓑ Ⓒ Ⓓ
8. Ⓕ Ⓖ Ⓗ Ⓙ
9. Ⓐ Ⓑ Ⓒ Ⓓ
10. Ⓕ Ⓖ Ⓗ Ⓙ
11. Ⓐ Ⓑ Ⓒ Ⓓ
12. Ⓕ Ⓖ Ⓗ Ⓙ
13. Ⓐ Ⓑ
14. Ⓐ Ⓑ
15. Ⓐ Ⓑ
16. Ⓐ Ⓑ
17. Ⓐ Ⓑ Ⓒ Ⓓ
18. Ⓕ Ⓖ Ⓗ Ⓙ
19. Ⓐ Ⓑ Ⓒ Ⓓ
20. Ⓕ Ⓖ Ⓗ Ⓙ
21. Ⓐ Ⓑ Ⓒ Ⓓ
22. Ⓕ Ⓖ Ⓗ Ⓙ
23. Ⓐ Ⓑ Ⓒ Ⓓ
24. Ⓕ Ⓖ Ⓗ Ⓙ
25. Ⓐ Ⓑ Ⓒ Ⓓ
26. Ⓕ Ⓖ Ⓗ Ⓙ
27. Ⓐ Ⓑ Ⓒ Ⓓ
28. Ⓕ Ⓖ Ⓗ Ⓙ
29. Ⓐ Ⓑ Ⓒ Ⓓ
30. Ⓕ Ⓖ Ⓗ Ⓙ
31. Ⓐ Ⓑ Ⓒ Ⓓ
32. Ⓕ Ⓖ Ⓗ Ⓙ
33. Ⓐ Ⓑ Ⓒ Ⓓ
34. Ⓕ Ⓖ Ⓗ Ⓙ
35. Ⓐ Ⓑ Ⓒ Ⓓ
36. Ⓕ Ⓖ Ⓗ Ⓙ
37. Ⓐ Ⓑ Ⓒ Ⓓ
38. Ⓕ Ⓖ Ⓗ Ⓙ
39. Ⓐ Ⓑ Ⓒ Ⓓ
40. Ⓕ Ⓖ Ⓗ Ⓙ

Student Answer Sheets *(cont.)*

Social Studies: World History
Part II
Pages: 61–62

Test

1. Ⓐ Ⓑ Ⓒ Ⓓ
2. Ⓕ Ⓖ Ⓗ Ⓙ
3. Ⓐ Ⓑ Ⓒ Ⓓ
4. Ⓐ Ⓑ
5. Ⓐ Ⓑ
6. Ⓐ Ⓑ
7. Ⓐ Ⓑ
8. Ⓕ Ⓖ Ⓗ Ⓙ
9. Ⓕ Ⓖ Ⓗ Ⓙ
10. Ⓕ Ⓖ Ⓗ Ⓙ
11. Ⓕ Ⓖ Ⓗ Ⓙ
12. Ⓐ Ⓑ Ⓒ Ⓓ
13. Ⓐ Ⓑ Ⓒ Ⓓ
14. Ⓐ Ⓑ Ⓒ Ⓓ
15. Ⓐ Ⓑ Ⓒ Ⓓ
16. Ⓕ Ⓖ Ⓗ Ⓙ
17. Ⓐ Ⓑ Ⓒ Ⓓ
18. Ⓕ Ⓖ Ⓗ Ⓙ
19. Ⓐ Ⓑ Ⓒ Ⓓ
20. Ⓕ Ⓖ Ⓗ Ⓙ
21. Ⓐ Ⓑ Ⓒ Ⓓ
22. Ⓕ Ⓖ Ⓗ Ⓙ
23. Ⓐ Ⓑ Ⓒ Ⓓ
24. Ⓐ Ⓑ Ⓒ Ⓓ
25. Ⓕ Ⓖ Ⓗ Ⓙ
26. Ⓐ Ⓑ Ⓒ Ⓓ
27. Ⓕ Ⓖ Ⓗ Ⓙ
28. Ⓐ Ⓑ Ⓒ Ⓓ
29. Ⓕ Ⓖ Ⓗ Ⓙ

Social Studies: World History
Part III
Pages: 63–65

Test

1. Ⓐ Ⓑ Ⓒ Ⓓ
2. Ⓕ Ⓖ Ⓗ Ⓙ
3. Ⓐ Ⓑ Ⓒ Ⓓ
4. Ⓕ Ⓖ Ⓗ Ⓙ
5. Ⓐ Ⓑ Ⓒ Ⓓ
6. Ⓕ Ⓖ Ⓗ Ⓙ
7. Ⓐ Ⓑ Ⓒ Ⓓ
8. Ⓕ Ⓖ Ⓗ Ⓙ
9. Ⓐ Ⓑ Ⓒ Ⓓ
10. Ⓕ Ⓖ Ⓗ Ⓙ
11. Ⓐ Ⓑ
12. Ⓐ Ⓑ
13. Ⓐ Ⓑ
14. Ⓕ Ⓖ Ⓗ Ⓙ
15. Ⓐ Ⓑ Ⓒ Ⓓ
16. Ⓕ Ⓖ Ⓗ Ⓙ
17. Ⓐ Ⓑ Ⓒ Ⓓ
18. Ⓕ Ⓖ Ⓗ Ⓙ

Social Studies: World Geography
Page: 66

Test

1. Ⓐ Ⓑ Ⓒ Ⓓ
2. Ⓕ Ⓖ Ⓗ Ⓙ
3. Ⓐ Ⓑ Ⓒ Ⓓ
4. Ⓕ Ⓖ Ⓗ Ⓙ
5. Ⓐ Ⓑ Ⓒ Ⓓ
6. Ⓕ Ⓖ Ⓗ Ⓙ
7. Ⓐ Ⓑ Ⓒ Ⓓ
8. Ⓕ Ⓖ Ⓗ Ⓙ
9. Ⓐ Ⓑ Ⓒ Ⓓ
10. Ⓕ Ⓖ Ⓗ Ⓙ
11. Ⓐ Ⓑ Ⓒ Ⓓ
12. Ⓕ Ⓖ Ⓗ Ⓙ

Student Answer Sheets *(cont.)*

Social Studies: United States History
Pages: 67–69

Test

1. Ⓐ Ⓑ Ⓒ Ⓓ
2. Ⓕ Ⓖ Ⓗ Ⓙ
3. Ⓐ Ⓑ Ⓒ Ⓓ
4. Ⓕ Ⓖ Ⓗ Ⓙ
5. Ⓐ Ⓑ Ⓒ Ⓓ
6. Ⓕ Ⓖ Ⓗ Ⓙ
7. Ⓐ Ⓑ Ⓒ Ⓓ
8. Ⓕ Ⓖ Ⓗ Ⓙ
9. Ⓐ Ⓑ Ⓒ Ⓓ
10. Ⓕ Ⓖ Ⓗ Ⓙ
11. Ⓐ Ⓑ Ⓒ Ⓓ
12. Ⓕ Ⓖ Ⓗ Ⓙ
13. Ⓐ Ⓑ Ⓒ Ⓓ
14. Ⓕ Ⓖ Ⓗ Ⓙ
15. Ⓐ Ⓑ Ⓒ Ⓓ
16. Ⓕ Ⓖ Ⓗ Ⓙ
17. Ⓐ Ⓑ Ⓒ Ⓓ
18. Ⓕ Ⓖ Ⓗ Ⓙ
19. Ⓐ Ⓑ Ⓒ Ⓓ
20. Ⓕ Ⓖ Ⓗ Ⓙ
21. Ⓐ Ⓑ Ⓒ Ⓓ
22. Ⓕ Ⓖ Ⓗ Ⓙ
23. Ⓐ Ⓑ Ⓒ Ⓓ
24. Ⓕ Ⓖ Ⓗ Ⓙ
25. Ⓐ Ⓑ Ⓒ Ⓓ
26. Ⓕ Ⓖ Ⓗ Ⓙ
27. Ⓐ Ⓑ Ⓒ Ⓓ
28. Ⓕ Ⓖ Ⓗ Ⓙ
29. Ⓐ Ⓑ Ⓒ Ⓓ
30. Ⓕ Ⓖ Ⓗ Ⓙ
31. Ⓐ Ⓑ Ⓒ Ⓓ
32. Ⓕ Ⓖ Ⓗ Ⓙ
33. Ⓐ Ⓑ Ⓒ Ⓓ
34. Ⓕ Ⓖ Ⓗ Ⓙ
35. Ⓐ Ⓑ Ⓒ Ⓓ
36. Ⓕ Ⓖ Ⓗ Ⓙ
37. Ⓐ Ⓑ Ⓒ Ⓓ
38. Ⓕ Ⓖ Ⓗ Ⓙ
39. Ⓐ Ⓑ Ⓒ Ⓓ
40. Ⓕ Ⓖ Ⓗ Ⓙ

Fine Arts: Music, Dance, and Theater
Pages: 70–71

Test

1. Ⓐ Ⓑ Ⓒ Ⓓ
2. Ⓕ Ⓖ Ⓗ Ⓙ
3. Ⓐ Ⓑ Ⓒ Ⓓ
4. Ⓕ Ⓖ Ⓗ Ⓙ
5. Ⓐ Ⓑ Ⓒ Ⓓ
6. Ⓕ Ⓖ Ⓗ Ⓙ
7. Ⓐ Ⓑ Ⓒ Ⓓ
8. Ⓕ Ⓖ Ⓗ Ⓙ
9. Ⓐ Ⓑ Ⓒ Ⓓ
10. Ⓕ Ⓖ Ⓗ Ⓙ
11. Ⓐ Ⓑ Ⓒ Ⓓ
12. Ⓕ Ⓖ Ⓗ Ⓙ
13. Ⓐ Ⓑ Ⓒ Ⓓ
14. Ⓕ Ⓖ Ⓗ Ⓙ
15. Ⓐ Ⓑ Ⓒ Ⓓ
16. Ⓕ Ⓖ Ⓗ Ⓙ
17. Ⓐ Ⓑ Ⓒ Ⓓ
18. Ⓕ Ⓖ Ⓗ Ⓙ
19. Ⓐ Ⓑ Ⓒ Ⓓ
20. Ⓕ Ⓖ Ⓗ Ⓙ
21. Ⓐ Ⓑ Ⓒ Ⓓ
22. Ⓕ Ⓖ Ⓗ Ⓙ
23. Ⓐ Ⓑ Ⓒ Ⓓ
24. Ⓕ Ⓖ Ⓗ Ⓙ
25. Ⓐ Ⓑ Ⓒ Ⓓ
26. Ⓕ Ⓖ Ⓗ Ⓙ

Student Answer Sheets *(cont.)*

Computers and Technology:
Backround
Pages: 72–73

Test

1. Ⓐ Ⓑ Ⓒ Ⓓ
2. Ⓕ Ⓖ Ⓗ Ⓙ
3. Ⓐ Ⓑ Ⓒ Ⓓ
4. Ⓕ Ⓖ Ⓗ Ⓙ
5. Ⓐ Ⓑ Ⓒ Ⓓ
6. Ⓕ Ⓖ Ⓗ Ⓙ
7. Ⓐ Ⓑ Ⓒ Ⓓ
8. Ⓕ Ⓖ Ⓗ Ⓙ
9. Ⓐ Ⓑ Ⓒ Ⓓ
10. Ⓕ Ⓖ Ⓗ Ⓙ
11. Ⓐ Ⓑ Ⓒ Ⓓ
12. Ⓕ Ⓖ Ⓗ Ⓙ
13. Ⓐ Ⓑ Ⓒ Ⓓ
14. Ⓕ Ⓖ Ⓗ Ⓙ
15. Ⓐ Ⓑ Ⓒ Ⓓ
16. Ⓕ Ⓖ Ⓗ Ⓙ

Computers and Technology:
Vocabulary
Page: 74

Test

1. Ⓐ Ⓑ Ⓒ Ⓓ
2. Ⓕ Ⓖ Ⓗ Ⓙ
3. Ⓐ Ⓑ Ⓒ Ⓓ
4. Ⓕ Ⓖ Ⓗ Ⓙ
5. Ⓐ Ⓑ Ⓒ Ⓓ
6. Ⓕ Ⓖ Ⓗ Ⓙ
7. Ⓐ Ⓑ Ⓒ Ⓓ
8. Ⓕ Ⓖ Ⓗ Ⓙ
9. Ⓐ Ⓑ Ⓒ Ⓓ
10. Ⓕ Ⓖ Ⓗ Ⓙ
11. Ⓐ Ⓑ Ⓒ Ⓓ
12. Ⓕ Ⓖ Ⓗ Ⓙ
13. Ⓐ Ⓑ Ⓒ Ⓓ
14. Ⓕ Ⓖ Ⓗ Ⓙ

Answer Key

Language Arts: Reading Competencies
Page: 15

Test

1. Ⓐ ● Ⓒ Ⓓ
2. Ⓕ Ⓖ ● Ⓙ
3. Ⓐ Ⓑ Ⓒ ●
4. Ⓕ Ⓖ ● Ⓙ
5. Ⓐ ● Ⓒ Ⓓ
6. Ⓕ Ⓖ Ⓗ ●

Language Arts: Reading Competencies
Pages: 16–17

Test

1. Ⓐ ● Ⓒ Ⓓ
2. Ⓕ Ⓖ Ⓗ ●
3. Ⓐ ● Ⓒ Ⓓ
4. Ⓕ Ⓖ ● Ⓙ

Language Arts: Reading Competencies
Pages: 18–19

Test

1. Ⓐ Ⓑ Ⓒ ●
2. Ⓕ ● Ⓗ Ⓙ
3. Ⓐ Ⓑ Ⓒ ●
4. Ⓕ ● Ⓗ Ⓙ

Language Arts: Reading Competencies
Page: 20

Test

1. Ⓐ Ⓑ Ⓒ ●
2. Ⓕ Ⓖ Ⓗ ●
3. Ⓐ ● Ⓒ Ⓓ
4. Ⓕ ● Ⓗ Ⓙ
5. Ⓐ Ⓑ ● Ⓓ

Answer Key *(cont.)*

Language Arts: Reading Competencies
Pages: 21–22

Test

1. Ⓐ ● Ⓒ Ⓓ
2. ● Ⓖ Ⓗ Ⓙ
3. Ⓐ Ⓑ Ⓒ ●
4. Ⓕ Ⓖ ● Ⓙ

Language Arts: Writing Competencies
Pages: 23–27

Test

1. ● Ⓑ Ⓒ
2. Ⓕ ● Ⓗ
3. ● Ⓑ Ⓒ
4. Ⓕ Ⓖ ●
5. Ⓐ ● Ⓒ
6. Ⓕ ● Ⓗ
7. Ⓐ ● Ⓒ
8. Ⓕ Ⓖ ●
9. Ⓐ Ⓑ ●
10. Ⓕ Ⓖ ●
11. ● Ⓑ Ⓒ
12. Ⓕ Ⓖ ●
13. Ⓐ Ⓑ ●
14. Ⓕ ● Ⓗ
15. Ⓐ ● Ⓒ
16. Ⓕ ● Ⓗ
17. Ⓐ Ⓑ ●
18. Ⓕ Ⓖ ●
19. Ⓐ ● Ⓒ
20. Ⓕ Ⓖ ●
21. Ⓐ Ⓑ ●
22. Ⓕ Ⓖ ●
23. ● Ⓑ Ⓒ
24. Ⓕ Ⓖ ●
25. ● Ⓑ Ⓒ
26. ● Ⓖ Ⓗ
27. Ⓐ Ⓑ ●
28. Ⓕ Ⓖ ●
29. ● Ⓑ Ⓒ
30. Ⓕ Ⓖ ●
31. Ⓐ Ⓑ ●
32. ● Ⓖ Ⓗ
33. ● Ⓑ Ⓒ
34. ● Ⓖ Ⓗ
35. ● Ⓑ Ⓒ
36. Ⓕ ● Ⓗ
37. Ⓐ ● Ⓒ

Language Arts: Writing Competencies
Pages: 28–29

Test

Answers will vary.

Answer Key *(cont.)*

Language Arts: Library Research
Pages: 30–32

Test

1. Ⓐ ● Ⓒ Ⓓ
2. Ⓕ Ⓖ ● Ⓙ
3. Ⓐ Ⓑ ● Ⓓ
4. Ⓕ Ⓖ Ⓗ ●
5. Ⓐ ● Ⓒ Ⓓ
6. Ⓕ Ⓖ ● Ⓙ
7. Ⓐ Ⓑ Ⓒ ●
8. ● Ⓖ Ⓗ Ⓙ
9. Ⓐ ● Ⓒ Ⓓ
10. Ⓕ Ⓖ ● Ⓙ
11. Ⓐ Ⓑ ● Ⓓ
12. Ⓕ Ⓖ Ⓗ ●
13. Ⓐ Ⓑ Ⓒ ●
14. ● Ⓖ Ⓗ Ⓙ
15. Ⓐ Ⓑ Ⓒ ●
16. ● Ⓖ Ⓗ
17. Ⓐ ● Ⓒ
18. Ⓕ Ⓖ ●
19. ● Ⓑ Ⓒ
20. Ⓕ Ⓖ ●
21. Ⓐ Ⓑ ● Ⓓ
22. ● Ⓖ Ⓗ Ⓙ
23. ● Ⓑ Ⓒ Ⓓ
24. Ⓕ ● Ⓗ Ⓙ
25. ● Ⓑ Ⓒ Ⓓ
26. Ⓕ Ⓖ Ⓗ ●

Mathematics: Rational and Irrational Numbers
Page: 35

Test

1. ● Ⓑ
2. Ⓐ ●
3. Ⓐ ●
4. Ⓐ ●
5. Ⓐ ●
6. Ⓐ ●
7. Ⓐ Ⓑ ● Ⓓ
8. ● Ⓖ Ⓗ Ⓙ
9. Ⓐ Ⓑ Ⓒ ●
10. Ⓕ Ⓖ ● Ⓙ
11. ● Ⓑ Ⓒ Ⓓ
12. Ⓕ Ⓖ Ⓗ ●

Mathematics: Real Numbers Part I
Pages: 36–37

Test

1. Ⓐ Ⓑ ● Ⓓ
2. ● Ⓖ Ⓗ Ⓙ
3. Ⓐ Ⓑ Ⓒ ●
4. Ⓕ ● Ⓗ Ⓙ
5. Ⓐ Ⓑ ● Ⓓ
6. Ⓕ Ⓖ ● Ⓙ
7. Ⓐ ● Ⓒ Ⓓ
8. Ⓕ Ⓖ ● Ⓙ
9. ● Ⓑ Ⓒ Ⓓ
10. Ⓕ Ⓖ ● Ⓙ
11. Ⓐ Ⓑ Ⓒ ●
12. ● Ⓖ Ⓗ Ⓙ
13. Ⓐ ● Ⓒ Ⓓ
14. Ⓕ Ⓖ ● Ⓙ
15. Ⓐ Ⓑ Ⓒ ●
16. ● Ⓖ Ⓗ Ⓙ
17. Ⓐ Ⓑ Ⓒ ●
18. Ⓕ ● Ⓗ Ⓙ
19. Ⓐ Ⓑ ● Ⓓ
20. Ⓕ ● Ⓗ Ⓙ
21. ● Ⓑ Ⓒ Ⓓ
22. Ⓕ Ⓖ ● Ⓙ
23. Ⓐ Ⓑ ● Ⓓ

Answer Key *(cont.)*

Mathematics: Real Numbers
Part II
Pages: 38–40

Test

1. Ⓐ ● Ⓒ Ⓓ
2. Ⓕ Ⓖ ● Ⓙ
3. Ⓐ ● Ⓒ Ⓓ
4. ● Ⓖ Ⓗ Ⓙ
5. Ⓐ Ⓑ ● Ⓓ
6. Ⓕ ● Ⓗ Ⓙ
7. Ⓐ Ⓑ ● Ⓓ
8. ● Ⓖ Ⓗ Ⓙ
9. Ⓐ Ⓑ Ⓒ ●
10. Ⓕ ● Ⓗ Ⓙ
11. Ⓐ Ⓑ Ⓒ ●
12. ● Ⓖ Ⓗ Ⓙ
13. Ⓐ Ⓑ ● Ⓓ
14. ● Ⓖ Ⓗ Ⓙ
15. Ⓐ Ⓑ ● Ⓓ
16. Ⓕ Ⓖ ● Ⓙ
17. Ⓐ ● Ⓒ Ⓓ
18. ● Ⓖ Ⓗ Ⓙ
19. Ⓐ Ⓑ ● Ⓓ
20. Ⓕ Ⓖ ● Ⓙ
21. Ⓐ ● Ⓒ Ⓓ
22. Ⓕ Ⓖ ● Ⓙ
23. Ⓐ ● Ⓒ Ⓓ
24. ● Ⓖ Ⓗ Ⓙ
25. Ⓐ Ⓑ ● Ⓓ
26. Ⓕ ● Ⓗ Ⓙ
27. Ⓐ Ⓑ ● Ⓓ
28. ● Ⓖ Ⓗ Ⓙ
29. Ⓐ Ⓑ ● Ⓓ
30. Ⓐ ●
31. Ⓐ ●
32. Ⓐ ●
33. ● Ⓑ
34. ● Ⓑ
35. ● Ⓑ
36. Ⓕ Ⓖ ● Ⓙ
37. ● Ⓑ Ⓒ Ⓓ
38. Ⓕ Ⓖ Ⓗ ●
39. Ⓐ Ⓑ ● Ⓓ
40. Ⓕ ● Ⓗ Ⓙ

Mathematics: Geometry
Page: 41

Test

1. Ⓐ Ⓑ ● Ⓓ
2. Ⓕ Ⓖ ● Ⓙ
3. Ⓐ ● Ⓒ Ⓓ
4. ● Ⓖ Ⓗ Ⓙ
5. ● Ⓑ Ⓒ Ⓓ
6. Ⓕ Ⓖ Ⓗ ●
7. Ⓐ Ⓑ Ⓒ ●
8. Ⓕ ● Ⓗ Ⓙ
9. Ⓐ Ⓑ ● Ⓓ
10. Ⓕ ● Ⓗ Ⓙ
11. Ⓐ ● Ⓒ Ⓓ
12. Ⓕ Ⓖ Ⓗ ●
13. Ⓐ ● Ⓒ Ⓓ
14. Ⓕ ● Ⓗ Ⓙ

Mathematics: Pre-Algebra
Page: 42

Test

1. Ⓐ Ⓑ ● Ⓓ
2. ● Ⓖ Ⓗ Ⓙ
3. Ⓐ ● Ⓒ Ⓓ
4. Ⓕ ● Ⓗ Ⓙ
5. Ⓐ Ⓑ ● Ⓓ
6. Ⓕ ● Ⓗ Ⓙ
7. Ⓐ Ⓑ ● Ⓓ
8. Ⓕ ● Ⓗ Ⓙ
9. Ⓐ Ⓑ Ⓒ ●
10. Ⓕ Ⓖ ● Ⓙ

Answer Key *(cont.)*

Science: Biology
Pages: 45–48

Test

1. Ⓐ Ⓑ ● Ⓓ
2. Ⓕ ● Ⓗ Ⓙ
3. Ⓐ ● Ⓒ Ⓓ
4. ● Ⓖ Ⓗ Ⓙ
5. ● Ⓑ Ⓒ Ⓓ
6. Ⓕ Ⓖ Ⓗ ●
7. Ⓐ Ⓑ ● Ⓓ
8. Ⓕ Ⓖ Ⓗ ●
9. ● Ⓑ
10. Ⓐ ●
11. ● Ⓑ
12. ● Ⓑ
13. Ⓐ ●
14. Ⓐ ●
15. Ⓐ ● Ⓒ Ⓓ
16. Ⓕ Ⓖ ● Ⓙ
17. Ⓐ ● Ⓒ Ⓓ
18. ● Ⓖ Ⓗ Ⓙ
19. Ⓐ Ⓑ Ⓒ ●
20. Ⓕ Ⓖ Ⓗ ●
21. Ⓐ ●
22. Ⓐ ●
23. Ⓐ ●

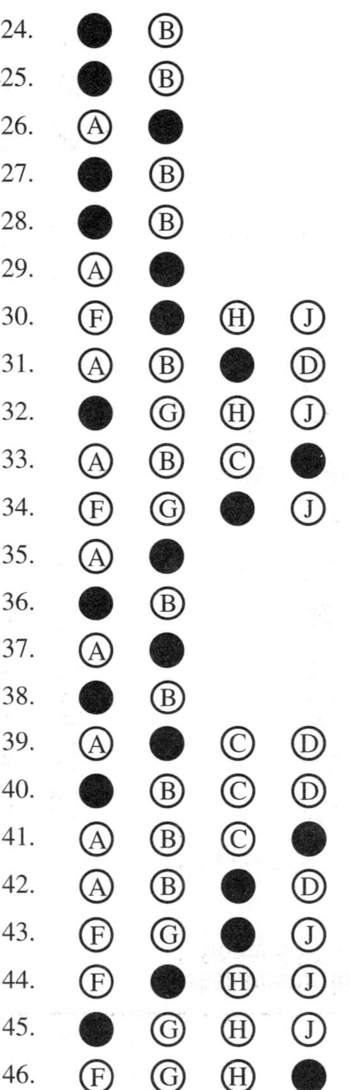

24. ● Ⓑ
25. ● Ⓑ
26. Ⓐ ●
27. ● Ⓑ
28. ● Ⓑ
29. Ⓐ ●
30. Ⓕ ● Ⓗ Ⓙ
31. Ⓐ Ⓑ ● Ⓓ
32. ● Ⓖ Ⓗ Ⓙ
33. Ⓐ Ⓑ Ⓒ ●
34. Ⓕ Ⓖ ● Ⓙ
35. Ⓐ ●
36. ● Ⓑ
37. Ⓐ ●
38. ● Ⓑ
39. Ⓐ ● Ⓒ Ⓓ
40. ● Ⓑ Ⓒ Ⓓ
41. Ⓐ Ⓑ Ⓒ ●
42. Ⓐ Ⓑ ● Ⓓ
43. Ⓕ Ⓖ ● Ⓙ
44. Ⓕ ● Ⓗ Ⓙ
45. ● Ⓖ Ⓗ Ⓙ
46. Ⓕ Ⓖ Ⓗ ●

47. Ⓐ Ⓑ Ⓒ ●
48. Ⓐ ● Ⓒ Ⓓ
49. Ⓐ Ⓑ ● Ⓓ
50. ● Ⓑ Ⓒ Ⓓ
51. Ⓕ ● Ⓗ Ⓙ
52. Ⓕ Ⓖ Ⓗ ●
53. ● Ⓖ Ⓗ Ⓙ
54. Ⓕ Ⓖ ● Ⓙ
55. Ⓐ Ⓑ Ⓒ ●
56. Ⓐ Ⓑ ● Ⓓ
57. ● Ⓑ Ⓒ Ⓓ
58. Ⓐ ● Ⓒ Ⓓ

Answer Key *(cont.)*

Science: Chemistry
Pages: 49–50

Test

1. Ⓐ Ⓑ ● Ⓓ
2. ● Ⓖ Ⓗ Ⓙ
3. Ⓐ ● Ⓒ Ⓓ
4. Ⓕ Ⓖ ● Ⓙ
5. Ⓐ ● Ⓒ Ⓓ
6. Ⓕ Ⓖ Ⓗ ●
7. Ⓐ Ⓑ ● Ⓓ
8. Ⓕ ● Ⓗ Ⓙ
9. ● Ⓑ Ⓒ Ⓓ
10. Ⓕ Ⓖ Ⓗ ●
11. Ⓐ Ⓑ ● Ⓓ
12. Ⓕ ● Ⓗ Ⓙ
13. Ⓐ Ⓑ ● Ⓓ
14. Ⓕ ● Ⓗ Ⓙ
15. Ⓐ ●
16. ● Ⓑ
17. ● Ⓑ
18. Ⓐ ●
19. Ⓐ ●
20. Ⓐ ●
21. ● Ⓑ
22. Ⓐ ●
23. ● Ⓑ Ⓒ
24. ● Ⓑ Ⓒ
25. Ⓐ Ⓑ ●
26. ● Ⓑ Ⓒ
27. Ⓐ Ⓑ ●
28. Ⓐ ● Ⓒ
29. Ⓐ ● Ⓒ
30. Ⓐ ● Ⓒ

Science: Physics
Pages: 51–53

Test

1. Ⓐ Ⓑ Ⓒ ●
2. Ⓕ Ⓖ ● Ⓙ
3. Ⓐ Ⓑ Ⓒ ●
4. Ⓕ Ⓖ ● Ⓙ
5. ● Ⓑ
6. Ⓐ ●
7. ● Ⓑ
8. Ⓐ ●
9. ● Ⓑ
10. Ⓕ Ⓖ Ⓗ ●
11. Ⓐ ● Ⓒ Ⓓ
12. Ⓕ ● Ⓗ Ⓙ
13. ● Ⓑ Ⓒ Ⓓ
14. Ⓕ ● Ⓗ Ⓙ
15. Ⓐ Ⓑ ● Ⓓ
16. Ⓕ Ⓖ ● Ⓙ
17. Ⓐ Ⓑ Ⓒ ●
18. ● Ⓖ Ⓗ Ⓙ
19. Ⓐ ● Ⓒ Ⓓ
20. Ⓕ Ⓖ Ⓗ ●
21. ● Ⓑ
22. ● Ⓑ
23. Ⓐ ●
24. ● Ⓑ
25. Ⓐ ●
26. Ⓐ ●
27. ● Ⓑ
28. Ⓕ ● Ⓗ Ⓙ
29. Ⓐ ● Ⓒ Ⓓ
30. Ⓕ ● Ⓗ Ⓙ
31. Ⓐ Ⓑ ● Ⓓ
32. Ⓕ Ⓖ ● Ⓙ
33. Ⓐ Ⓑ Ⓒ ●
34. ● Ⓖ Ⓗ Ⓙ
35. ● Ⓑ Ⓒ Ⓓ
36. Ⓕ Ⓖ ● Ⓙ
37. Ⓐ ● Ⓒ Ⓓ
38. Ⓕ Ⓖ Ⓗ ●
39. Ⓐ Ⓑ ● Ⓓ
40. Ⓕ ● Ⓗ Ⓙ

Answer Key *(cont.)*

Science: Geology
Pages: 54–55

Test

#				
1.	Ⓐ	Ⓑ	Ⓒ	●
2.	Ⓕ	Ⓖ	●	Ⓙ
3.	Ⓐ	●	Ⓒ	Ⓓ
4.	Ⓕ	●	Ⓗ	Ⓙ
5.	Ⓐ	Ⓑ	●	Ⓓ
6.	Ⓕ	●	Ⓗ	Ⓙ
7.	Ⓐ	Ⓑ	●	Ⓓ
8.	Ⓕ	Ⓖ	Ⓗ	●
9.	Ⓐ	●	Ⓒ	Ⓓ
10.	Ⓕ	Ⓖ	●	Ⓙ
11.	Ⓐ	●	Ⓒ	Ⓓ
12.	Ⓕ	Ⓖ	●	Ⓙ
13.	●	Ⓑ	Ⓒ	Ⓓ
14.	Ⓕ	●	Ⓗ	Ⓙ
15.	Ⓐ	Ⓑ	●	Ⓓ
16.	Ⓕ	Ⓖ	Ⓗ	●
17.	Ⓐ	●		
18.	Ⓐ	●		
19.	Ⓐ	●		
20.	●	Ⓑ		
21.	Ⓐ	●		
22.	Ⓐ	●		
23.	Ⓐ	●		

Social Studies: World History
Part I
Pages: 58–60

Test

#				
1.	Ⓐ	Ⓑ	●	Ⓓ
2.	Ⓕ	●	Ⓗ	Ⓙ
3.	Ⓐ	●	Ⓒ	Ⓓ
4.	Ⓕ	●	Ⓗ	Ⓙ
5.	Ⓐ	●	Ⓒ	Ⓓ
6.	Ⓕ	Ⓖ	●	Ⓙ
7.	Ⓐ	Ⓑ	Ⓒ	●
8.	Ⓕ	●	Ⓗ	Ⓙ
9.	Ⓐ	Ⓑ	Ⓒ	●
10.	Ⓕ	●	Ⓗ	Ⓙ
11.	Ⓐ	●	Ⓒ	Ⓓ
12.	Ⓕ	Ⓖ	●	Ⓙ
13.	●	Ⓑ		
14.	Ⓐ	●		
15.	Ⓐ	●		
16.	●	Ⓑ		
17.	Ⓐ	●	Ⓒ	Ⓓ
18.	Ⓕ	Ⓖ	●	Ⓙ
19.	●	Ⓑ	Ⓒ	Ⓓ
20.	Ⓕ	Ⓖ	Ⓗ	●
21.	Ⓐ	●	Ⓒ	Ⓓ
22.	Ⓕ	Ⓖ	●	Ⓙ
23.	Ⓐ	Ⓑ	●	Ⓓ
24.	Ⓕ	●	Ⓗ	Ⓙ
25.	Ⓐ	●	Ⓒ	Ⓓ
26.	Ⓕ	●	Ⓗ	Ⓙ
27.	Ⓐ	●	Ⓒ	Ⓓ
28.	Ⓕ	Ⓖ	Ⓗ	●
29.	Ⓐ	●	Ⓒ	Ⓓ
30.	Ⓕ	●	Ⓗ	Ⓙ
31.	Ⓐ	Ⓑ	Ⓒ	●
32.	Ⓕ	●	Ⓗ	Ⓙ
33.	Ⓐ	●	Ⓒ	Ⓓ
34.	Ⓕ	Ⓖ	●	Ⓙ
35.	Ⓐ	Ⓑ	Ⓒ	●
36.	Ⓕ	●	Ⓗ	Ⓙ
37.	Ⓐ	Ⓑ	●	Ⓓ
38.	Ⓕ	Ⓖ	Ⓗ	●
39.	Ⓐ	●	Ⓒ	Ⓓ
40.	Ⓕ	Ⓖ	●	Ⓙ

Answer Key *(cont.)*

Social Studies: World History
Part II
Pages: 61–62

Test

1. Ⓐ ● Ⓒ Ⓓ
2. Ⓕ Ⓖ ● Ⓙ
3. Ⓐ ● Ⓒ Ⓓ
4. ● Ⓑ
5. Ⓐ ●
6. ● Ⓑ
7. ● Ⓑ
8. Ⓕ Ⓖ ● Ⓙ
9. ● Ⓖ Ⓗ Ⓙ
10. Ⓕ Ⓖ Ⓗ ●
11. Ⓕ ● Ⓗ Ⓙ
12. Ⓐ Ⓑ ● Ⓓ
13. Ⓐ ● Ⓒ Ⓓ
14. Ⓐ Ⓑ Ⓒ ●
15. ● Ⓑ Ⓒ Ⓓ
16. Ⓕ Ⓖ ● Ⓙ
17. Ⓐ ● Ⓒ Ⓓ
18. Ⓕ Ⓖ Ⓗ ●
19. ● Ⓑ Ⓒ Ⓓ
20. Ⓕ ● Ⓗ Ⓙ
21. Ⓐ ● Ⓒ Ⓓ
22. Ⓕ ● Ⓗ Ⓙ
23. Ⓐ Ⓑ ● Ⓓ
24. Ⓕ ● Ⓗ Ⓙ
25. Ⓐ Ⓑ Ⓒ ●
26. Ⓕ Ⓖ ● Ⓙ
27. Ⓐ ● Ⓒ Ⓓ
28. ● Ⓖ Ⓗ Ⓙ
29. Ⓐ ● Ⓒ Ⓓ

Social Studies: World History
Part III
Pages: 63–65

Test

1. Ⓐ Ⓑ ● Ⓓ
2. Ⓕ ● Ⓗ Ⓙ
3. Ⓐ ● Ⓒ Ⓓ
4. ● Ⓖ Ⓗ Ⓙ
5. Ⓐ ● Ⓒ Ⓓ
6. Ⓕ Ⓖ Ⓗ ●
7. Ⓐ Ⓑ ● Ⓓ
8. Ⓕ ● Ⓗ Ⓙ
9. Ⓐ Ⓑ Ⓒ ●
10. Ⓕ Ⓖ ● Ⓙ
11. Ⓐ ●
12. Ⓐ ●
13. ● Ⓑ
14. Ⓕ ● Ⓗ Ⓙ
15. Ⓐ ● Ⓒ Ⓓ
16. Ⓕ Ⓖ Ⓗ ●
17. Ⓐ Ⓑ ● Ⓓ
18. Ⓕ Ⓖ Ⓗ ●

Social Studies: World Geography
Page: 66

Test

1. Ⓐ Ⓑ ● Ⓓ
2. ● Ⓖ Ⓗ Ⓙ
3. Ⓐ ● Ⓒ Ⓓ
4. Ⓕ Ⓖ ● Ⓙ
5. Ⓐ ● Ⓒ Ⓓ
6. Ⓕ Ⓖ Ⓗ ●
7. Ⓐ ● Ⓒ Ⓓ
8. Ⓕ Ⓖ ● Ⓙ
9. Ⓐ Ⓑ ● Ⓓ
10. Ⓕ ● Ⓗ Ⓙ
11. ● Ⓑ Ⓒ Ⓓ
12. Ⓕ ● Ⓗ Ⓙ

Answer Key *(cont.)*

Social Studies: United States History
Pages: 67–69

Test

1. Ⓐ ● Ⓒ Ⓓ
2. Ⓕ ● Ⓗ Ⓙ
3. ● Ⓑ Ⓒ Ⓓ
4. Ⓕ Ⓖ ● Ⓙ
5. Ⓐ Ⓑ Ⓒ ●
6. ● Ⓖ Ⓗ Ⓙ
7. Ⓐ Ⓑ ● Ⓓ
8. Ⓕ Ⓖ Ⓗ ●
9. Ⓐ ● Ⓒ Ⓓ
10. ● Ⓖ Ⓗ Ⓙ
11. Ⓐ Ⓑ ● Ⓓ
12. Ⓕ Ⓖ ● Ⓙ
13. ● Ⓑ Ⓒ Ⓓ
14. Ⓕ ● Ⓗ Ⓙ
15. Ⓐ Ⓑ Ⓒ ●
16. Ⓕ Ⓖ Ⓗ ●
17. Ⓐ Ⓑ Ⓒ ●
18. Ⓕ ● Ⓗ Ⓙ
19. Ⓐ ● Ⓒ Ⓓ
20. Ⓕ Ⓖ ● Ⓙ
21. Ⓐ Ⓑ ● Ⓓ
22. Ⓕ Ⓖ Ⓗ ●
23. ● Ⓑ Ⓒ Ⓓ
24. ● Ⓖ Ⓗ Ⓙ
25. Ⓐ ● Ⓒ Ⓓ
26. Ⓕ ● Ⓗ Ⓙ
27. ● Ⓑ Ⓒ Ⓓ
28. Ⓕ Ⓖ Ⓗ ●
29. Ⓐ Ⓑ Ⓒ ●
30. ● Ⓖ Ⓗ Ⓙ
31. Ⓐ Ⓑ ● Ⓓ
32. Ⓕ Ⓖ ● Ⓙ
33. Ⓐ Ⓑ Ⓒ ●
34. Ⓕ Ⓖ Ⓗ ●
35. ● Ⓑ Ⓒ Ⓓ
36. ● Ⓖ Ⓗ Ⓙ
37. Ⓐ Ⓑ ● Ⓓ
38. Ⓕ ● Ⓗ Ⓙ
39. Ⓐ ● Ⓒ Ⓓ
40. Ⓕ Ⓖ ● Ⓙ

Fine Arts: Music, Dance, and Theater
Pages: 70–71

Test

1. Ⓐ Ⓑ ● Ⓓ
2. Ⓕ ● Ⓗ Ⓙ
3. Ⓐ Ⓑ Ⓒ ●
4. Ⓕ Ⓖ ● Ⓙ
5. Ⓐ ● Ⓒ Ⓓ
6. Ⓕ Ⓖ Ⓗ ●
7. Ⓐ ● Ⓒ Ⓓ
8. ● Ⓖ Ⓗ Ⓙ
9. Ⓐ Ⓑ Ⓒ ●
10. Ⓕ Ⓖ Ⓗ ●
11. Ⓐ ● Ⓒ Ⓓ
12. Ⓕ Ⓖ ● Ⓙ
13. Ⓐ ● Ⓒ Ⓓ
14. Ⓕ ● Ⓗ Ⓙ
15. Ⓐ Ⓑ ● Ⓓ
16. Ⓕ ● Ⓗ Ⓙ
17. Ⓐ ● Ⓒ Ⓓ
18. Ⓕ Ⓖ Ⓗ ●
19. Ⓐ Ⓑ ● Ⓓ
20. Ⓕ ● Ⓗ Ⓙ
21. Ⓐ ● Ⓒ Ⓓ
22. Ⓕ Ⓖ Ⓗ ●
23. Ⓐ ● Ⓒ Ⓓ
24. Ⓕ Ⓖ Ⓗ ●
25. ● Ⓑ Ⓒ Ⓓ
26. Ⓕ Ⓖ ● Ⓙ

Answer Key *(cont.)*

Computers and Technology: Background
Pages: 72–73

Test

1.	Ⓐ	●	Ⓒ	Ⓓ
2.	Ⓕ	Ⓖ	●	Ⓙ
3.	Ⓐ	●	Ⓒ	Ⓓ
4.	●	Ⓖ	Ⓗ	Ⓙ
5.	Ⓐ	Ⓑ	●	Ⓓ
6.	Ⓕ	Ⓖ	Ⓗ	●
7.	Ⓐ	●	Ⓒ	Ⓓ
8.	Ⓕ	Ⓖ	●	Ⓙ
9.	Ⓐ	●	Ⓒ	Ⓓ
10.	Ⓕ	●	Ⓗ	Ⓙ
11.	●	Ⓑ	Ⓒ	Ⓓ
12.	Ⓕ	●	Ⓗ	Ⓙ
13.	Ⓐ	Ⓑ	●	Ⓓ
14.	Ⓕ	Ⓖ	Ⓗ	●
15.	Ⓐ	●	Ⓒ	Ⓓ
16.	Ⓕ	Ⓖ	Ⓗ	●

Computers and Technology: Vocabulary
Page: 74

Test

1.	Ⓐ	●	Ⓒ	Ⓓ
2.	●	Ⓖ	Ⓗ	Ⓙ
3.	Ⓐ	Ⓑ	●	Ⓓ
4.	●	Ⓖ	Ⓗ	Ⓙ
5.	Ⓐ	Ⓑ	Ⓒ	●
6.	Ⓕ	●	Ⓗ	Ⓙ
7.	Ⓐ	Ⓑ	●	Ⓓ
8.	●	Ⓖ	Ⓗ	Ⓙ
9.	Ⓐ	Ⓑ	Ⓒ	●
10.	Ⓕ	Ⓖ	●	Ⓙ
11.	Ⓐ	●	Ⓒ	Ⓓ
12.	●	Ⓖ	Ⓗ	Ⓙ
13.	Ⓐ	Ⓑ	Ⓒ	●
14.	Ⓕ	Ⓖ	●	Ⓙ